MW00904043

The Ultimate Book for Overcoming Dyslexia - Tools for Kids, Teenagers & Adults

A dyslexia empowerment plan & solutions tool kit for tutors and parents to provide dyslexia help for kids & adults

Jessica Caplain

to get more than a dozen parallel and complementary audio/video/book courses to this title.

The downloadable Premium Courses are **worth over a thousand dollars**, which you will get **ALL FOR FREE!**
-- Mind Power Mastery GOLD
-- How To Develop Emotional Intelligence-
-- What To Do Against Stress Buildup
-- Fearless You
-- Emotional Equilibrium
-- The Mindset Transformation Course
-- The Stress Extinguisher Course
-- The Warrior's Mindset Course
-- Several Unannounced titles
-- Dealing with Sorrow
-- 5 Ways to Calm your Mind
-- Breaking Bad Habits - DELUXE Package
-- The Psychology of Motivation Course

Introduction

You have chosen this book because you are concerned about your child. He or she is not keeping up in class, makes spelling errors, and hates to read even the simplest words. Is your child dyslexic? Should you get an assessment? What can you do to help him or her do better in reading and writing? You need straightforward and practical advice.

What's in this book?

In this book, you will gain relevant information on dyslexia. You will not be buried with a mountain of theories or be lost in terminology. You will read only truthful information about things that matter.

You will get ideas on hands-on activities that your child can do right away, as well as strategies that are beneficial for his or her lifetime. There are plenty of handy tips for dealing with your child's daily problems, too, such as how to help him or her stay organized and keeping the b's and d's facing the correct way. You will also get the scoop on things such as note-taking techniques, college application tips, and helpful advice on how to succeed in the workforce for teens and adults.

You are probably just starting to consider dyslexia or may have already done your homework. Your child's Individualized Education Program (IEP) may already be underway, or you have never heard of it at all. Whether you want reassurance, legal details made easy, or practical strategies, this book is for you. Immerse yourself chapter by chapter, as you like. All the chapters in this book will follow a logical progression.

You will also find tons of information here to help you get the guidance you have been looking for. Whatever your needs and wants currently are, you will love this book because you will get all the handy stuff to prepare yourself and your child for a colorful journey ahead.

Catch a glimpse

This book has five parts, all filled to the brim with details on dyslexia.

Chapter I: Dyslexia Defined

This part will tell you what exactly dyslexia does and does not mean. The "does not" part is essential because, like many educators point out, the term gets so overused that its meaning can become obscured. In this chapter, you will also learn the causes and types of dyslexia, as well as an overview of the symptoms to watch out for at any age.

Chapter II: Knowing When to Seek Help

This part will give you more time to look more closely at the signs of dyslexia. You will have the chance to examine your child's behavior during preschool and school years. It will also show you how and when to get an assessment for your child.

Chapter III: Exploring Your Options

This part talks about your child's everyday struggle in class. It will answer your concern about whether your child would ever do better in another class or school or how much does private tutoring costs. You will also learn about learning centers that are dyslexia-friendly and how to ensure that your child has a good IEP. This chapter will give you tips on how to help your child make his or her schoolwork easier, even when there is no IEP.

Chapter IV: Doing Your Part in Your Child's Treatment

Most treatment for dyslexia involves phonics-based and multisensory instruction. If you are unsure what these are, it is totally fine and normal. This part of the book explains it all in the simplest and straightforward terms that you will feel completely comfortable with. You will also know about the methods of visualizing, memorizing, and rhyming to help your child read better. This chapter will show you how to establish a healthy and fun reading routine and provide you tips to help your child complete daily tasks with ease.

Chapter V: Dyslexia Beyond the Childhood Years

In the past few decades, anyone who has been through high school has heard about things such as community service, portfolios, and college entrance exams. In this part, you will learn what people with dyslexia do to make specific tasks less formidable when applying for college. You will also get the lowdown on helping your child adjust to the teenage years and discover how adult dyslexics can become more successful in the real world.

What now?

If you are unsure whether your child needs an assessment for possible dyslexia, then you have come to the right place. This book has everything that you need to know and what you have to do. You will learn to enjoy and appreciate your child's journey as you read through this book.

Take your time, and mull over the points that apply to you. This book will serve as your map for guiding your child forward. In the real world, people want to hear the truth, which is why, in this book, you will only get the plain and simple truth on dyslexia. Think of this book as your comprehensive tour of the definitions, terminologies, treatments, and programs that you can learn to help your child succeed through adulthood.

Chapter I: Dyslexia Defined

A lot of children have difficulty reading and writing. They eventually catch up after months of extra help. There are times when the problem disappears without any intervention. Dyslexia is not like that.

A child with dyslexia shows unexpected writing and reading difficulties. He or she may be bright, and you provide all the extra help, but he or she just does not get it. Your child will probably learn to write and read at age 10, but you might notice the need to reread texts many times before full comprehension is achieved. If you think your child may have dyslexia, then continue reading.

Common misconceptions

There are a lot of misconceptions about dyslexia that you need to know. Here are some of them:

>Brain damage
>Stupidity
>Willfulness
>Retardation
>Distractibility
>Laziness

Research shows that dyslexic patients use a different portion of their brain when they read more than non-dyslexics. This condition also tends to be hereditary. Some psychologists have even broken it down into several types, including visual dyslexia and phonological dyslexia.

Symptoms

Some practitioners never use "dyslexia" to describe the condition. Psychologists, however, look for a bunch of symptoms to confirm a diagnosis. These symptoms show up at different ages, as well.

A dyslexic preschooler will exhibit the following behaviors:
>Starts to speak late. No actual speech until after the age of 2.
>Utters muddled-up words, like "gabrage" for garbage.
>Does not enjoy reading or being read to.
>Cannot tell rhyming words and cannot differentiate letters and squiggles or symbols.

A dyslexic school-age child, on the other hand, will show the following behaviors:
>Writes words with the letters jumbled up
>Writes words that are barely legible
>Reverses numbers and letters
>Has difficulty re-telling a story
>Leaves out or adds small words when reading

Dyslexia, unless hereditary, can hit you all of a sudden. Your child may seem fine, but any sign of stumbling means he or she may have dyslexia. Bear in mind that teens and adults left undiagnosed also exhibit common signs, such as avoidance of reading and writing.

When to have your child tested

It is best to seek professional help than waste precious months or years wondering whether your child has learning difficulties. If it appears that your child has dyslexia or other learning problems, it will be wise to get him or her treated right away. You will thank yourself for doing so later on.

That said, you cannot whisk your child off to an assessment before the age of 5 because dyslexia is mostly about your child's reading ability. When your child starts going to school and shows difficulty learning the alphabet and making speech sounds, it is time to have them assessed for early intervention.

Your child may undergo one or all of the following tests:
>Language tests
>Early screening tests
>Vision and hearing tests
>IQ tests
>A full test battery
>Performance tests

A psychologist conducts a full assessment for possible dyslexia. The public school district has a psychologist offering free services, but you may need to write a formal request for it. If you want a second opinion or outside help, then ask the district for a list of private psychologists within the area. It is a must to ensure that you are consulting a licensed professional to avoid misdiagnosis.

Private schools, however, do not automatically provide any of these services because they make autonomous decisions on how they test and treat dyslexia. They are also not legally obligated to offer assessment and an

Individualized Education Program, or IEP, for kids who need special education.

Programs to look for

Finding the best school for your child becomes challenging after being diagnosed with dyslexia. If the diagnosis makes him or her qualified for special education, then she can receive an IEP. Preparing for this program includes talking to your child's teacher, providing lists and essential documents, and ensuring ample support.

In public schools, you have the right to an IEP once your child is found to have dyslexia or any learning disability. You do not get this legal right in private schools, but you can still get help without this program. For example, you can stay in close contact with the teachers and enroll your child in tutoring programs, homework clubs, and extracurricular activities that help boost confidence.

Outside school, you can consider the following options to improve your child's reading and writing abilities:
>Dyslexia therapies
>Private, individual tutors
>Reading clinics that specialize in helping dyslexic people
>General learning centers

You can also help your child at home with their homework and set him or her up with plenty of handy gizmos.

What you can do at home

You can help your child manage dyslexia at home by keeping in mind these tips:

>Apply visualizing, memorizing, and rhyming tricks
>Enhance your knowledge of phonics
>Practice frequently
>Encourage multisensory activities
>Motivate your child to stay organized, tell time, and follow steps

Here are great reasons why you should help your dyslexic child at home:

>Your child may not begin to read until age 10. Clue in the teacher, so you are aware of what is going on. If your child can utter simple words, their learning difficulties may not show up until much later.

>When your child undergoes a hear-see-say-do routine with new concepts, they remember better. This routine is called multisensory learning. You can do this at home by making your child say things he or she wants to remember aloud and words she is copying down.

>Establishing a schedule that will allow your child to get homework done but still flexible enough for occasional PB&J dinner and play-offs can spark sporting and social interests. They may be necessary for your child because they provide an opportunity to excel.

Facts about dyslexia

Researchers found that dyslexia is, almost certainly, a brain problem. They have also discovered how it manifests in your child's behavior. The condition has a literal meaning, "trouble with words." Your child shows difficulty in reading, spelling, and writing.

The word dyslexia came from the Latin word "dys" (difficulty), and "lexis" (word). Your child may have other learning difficulties, too, such as understanding directional instructions and recalling words when speaking.

Here are a few more key points on dyslexia and its nature:

>It is a disorder that affects your child's reading and writing abilities. The child has trouble recognizing, sounding out, and spelling words.
>Dyslexic children also often lack other language skills, like remembering words he or she would like to use, or recalling a sequence of instructions or spoken words.
>A dyslexic child cannot process sounds in a word.
>The condition is lifelong, but its impact on one's life can be minimized through constant practice and learning.
>Its cause remains uncertain, but research shows definite differences in brain function between dyslexics and non-dyslexics.
>It affects a person's self-image, and it is easy for him or her to feel dumb and less capable.

Dyslexic children must learn to overcome or manage their problems, including their limitations and the ignorance and attitudes of people around them. While it is difficult to do, your child can handle his or her situation if he or she is aware of what's going on. Ensure that your child knows and understands that dyslexia is a brain problem, and how it makes it difficult for him or her to read, spell, write, and do other things like differentiating left from rate and recalling words in his memory.

Dyslexia as a Specific Learning Disability (SLD)

Dyslexia is a Specific Learning Disability, or SLD, because it affects certain learning aspects. These include reading, writing, articulation, auditory, nonverbal, dysgraphia, dyscalculia, and other learning disabilities that could coexist with dyslexia.

The International Dyslexia Association considers dyslexia an SLD, but many schools call the condition a Learning Disability (LD) or Specific Learning Disability (SLD) and not "dyslexia." Most school districts use the term SLD so teachers, in turn, can use it. The good thing about using the medical term to describe the condition is that it helps separate a dyslexic child from those with poor reading skills for other reasons. People who dislike using either term – SLD or dyslexia – talk about things like "learning difficulties" or "learning style issues."

Knowing the causes

According to the IDA, dyslexia is neurological. While brain mapping is a relatively new technology, experts agree that there are differences in brain activity between dyslexics and non-dyslexics.

In the brain map of a dyslexic individual:
>Parts of the brain's right hemisphere get busy during reading. A fluent reader uses mostly the left hemisphere.
>Brain activity begins to look more like that of a non-dyslexic when there is an improvement in the patient's reading skills.
>Dyslexics use their brain more than non-dyslexics when performing language activities.

Genetics

Only a couple of things are clear when it comes to the cause of dyslexia:
>It runs in the family
>Dyslexics use their brain differently than non-dyslexics

What is not clear is whether you inherit a "dyslexic brain" or your brain suddenly develops that way because of your inability to read. The brain is a complex organ. Most experts do believe that there is a genetic basis to the condition, and they are determining which gene/s is/are involved.

Types of dyslexia

You may be surprised, but there are many kinds of dyslexia. To get you one step ahead, here are the subtypes that you need to know:

>Phonological dyslexia: Also called auditory dyslexia, dysphonetic dyslexia, or dysphonesia, this type is the

most common. A child with phonological dyslexia has trouble matching letters to the sounds and identifying phonemes. He or she makes wild guesses when reading, and spelling is all over the place.

>Visual dyslexia: This type is also called surface dyslexia, dyseidetic dyslexia, or dyseidesia. If your child is having trouble with words that do not sound regularly, and have to learn mainly by sight, then he or she may have visual dyslexia. A child with dyseidesia reads extremely slow, and spells phonetically without realizing that his words appear to be wrong.

>Dysnomia: Also called naming-speed deficits, anomia, or semantic dyslexia, a child with this type of dyslexia has difficulty finding his or her words. He or she cannot always remember the correct word, despite having learned about it before, and says instead "the thingy" or other inappropriate words.

>Mixed dyslexia: This type is also called dysphneidetic dyslexia. It is a combination of visual and phonological dyslexia. Mixed dyslexics have the tendency to show severe reading deficits and cognitive functions like visual perception, visual-motor integration, and working memory.

>Severe and mild dyslexia: A dyslexic child can have mild or severe dyslexia. If the symptoms are mild, then he or she may not qualify for special education offered by the school. A psychologist can determine the extent of your child's dyslexia.

>Double deficit: This is the term used to describe a child with dysnomia and phonological dyslexia.

Dyslexia VS ADD and ADHD

Many dyslexic children have other conditions, too. Some of them have Attention Deficit Disorder (ADD) or Attention Deficit Hyperactivity Disorder (ADHD). A dyslexic child with either of these two conditions struggle to focus on what they are doing or attend to whoever is speaking to them The child feels fidgety and restless and may wander off when engaging in a conversation. He or she is challenging to stay on track in class, and the unsettling behavior can stir other children up.

ADHD and ADD share some of the symptoms of dyslexia. The American Psychiatric Association is equipped with a complex formula to assess your child better. However, the inital symptoms for ADD or ADHD are:

>Your child often makes careless mistakes and misses details
>Your child has difficulty completing a task
>Your child often does not listen to you
>Your child often does not follow instructions or complete tasks
>Your child is disorganized
>Your child does not want to start tasks that require his focus over time.
>Your child tends to lose things
>Your child gets distracted with most sounds, even small noises
>Your child tends to be forgetful.

If your child has ADHD, he or she will show ADD symptoms with a bit of hyperactivity. The American Psychiatric Association looks for impulsivity and hyperactivity symptoms to diagnose ADHD, such as:

A.Hyperactivity:
>Fidgeting
>Frequently leaving seat
>Runs instead of walking
>Climbs over furniture instead of behaving
>Has trouble playing quietly
>Described as a "live wire"
>Talks nonstop

B.Impulsivity:
>Cannot control excitement to talk
>Has difficulty waiting for his or her turn
>Always pushing in or interrupting

Your preschooler and signs of late development

The following list will give you the different kinds of behaviors that psychologists consider when they check for dyslexia symptoms in preschoolers:

>Delayed speech – no actual speech until after the age of 2
>Utters muddled up words
>Does not understand what you say until it is repeated several times
>Cannot follow more than one direction at a time
>Cannot remember words

>Takes time to get the words out
>Cannot name the letters of the alphabet
>Does not like being read to
>Likes being read to, but no interest is shown in letters or words
>Shows weak fine motor skills, like cutting, drawing, and threading
>Cannot tell rhyming words
>Cannot differentiate letters and squiggles or other symbols
>Cannot recognize own written name

The psychologist will assess your child and ask you whether he or she has/has had ear infections. They may not be signs of dyslexia, but they can be a complicating factor that could worsen dyslexia.

Dyslexia signs in your school-age child

You may notice the following behaviors in your child's dyslexia symptoms:

>Does not exhibit dominant handedness until around age 7
>Has immature speech
>Cannot write the alphabet
>Cannot tell the sounds of the alphabet
>Is verbal and bright but unusually weak at reading
>Uses advanced vocabulary when having difficulty recalling simpler words
>Leaves out or adds small words when reading
>Has difficulty re-telling a story.
>Complains of moving words or words running off the paper

>Complains of headache, dizziness, or stomach pains while reading
>Gets grades that do not match his or her intelligence
>Often uses words like "thingy" and "umm"
>Writes words, but the letters are in the wrong places
>Reverses numbers and letters
>Writing is nearly illegible
>Gets confused about directional instructions
>Does not follow through with chores involving multiple steps
>Performs poorly in writing, reading, and/or spelling
>Cannot recall facts, such as days of the week or multiplication table

Your child may also show signs of dyslexia that have no direct link to writing and reading. The behavior, attitude, and all-around manner could speak volumes. How should you react? Here are some typical dyslexic actions that you may notice:

>He or she seems unhappy
>He or she appears practically invisible or too quiet
>He or she stirs up a lot of trouble in school or at home
>He or she is disorganized

Visible signs in teens and adults

Dyslexia may be the cause when your teenage dislikes doing homework and going to school and hardly picks up a book. Teenagers with dyslexia may go to great lengths to dodge writing and reading tasks. They will find ways to cover up their writing and reading weaknesses.

Here are the things that you may notice in your dyslexic teenager:

>Avoids writing and reading
>Guesses words, shows little comprehension and skips small words
>Muddles up the letters inside the words or completely leaves them out
>Starts to dislike going to school
>Does not do homework
>Tells you that she feels dumb or could not care less
>Is more self-conscious than ever
>Does not like getting involved in as many social events as she once used to
>Is abusive, aggressive, or antisocial

Meanwhile, dyslexic adults have learned to live with their hindrances. Some would tell everyone about their dyslexia, and even joke about their goof ups. Some, however, would hide their difficulties and do anything to cover them up. Others do not have any idea that they have dyslexia.

The stereotypical dyslexic adult shows the following behavior:
>Avoids reading or writing
>Types or writes letters in the wrong order
>Reverses the numbers and dates, mostly 3s and 5s
>Cannot fill out forms
>Adept at covering up illiteracy by doing things, such as avoiding reading the menu or ordering what friends eat
>Has a bad attitude and/or low self-confidence
>Is a dropout
>Has a job below their potential
>Changes jobs more often than normal

>Misses the minor details when performing tasks
>Cannot play sports because of poor coordination
>Cannot read to own kids

Here are a few things that a dyslexic adult may be unable to read:

>Numbers of the salary check
>Instructions on prescription medicine
>Menu in a restaurant
>Numbers in the phone directory
>Street names, traffic signs, and maps
>Books, letters, books, and homework of child
>Instructions for building and/or using new equipment
>TV schedules

Taking action now

If you struggled at school or know that you are dyslexic, or if somebody else in the family fits the signs, then watch your child for dyslexia symptoms from an early age. If she does not have dyslexia, then you have lost nothing by simply watching her. If she does have it, then you have gained valuable time and insight.

You may be the only person to notice that your child needs help, and your action may spare you from that "I should have known" hindsight. The symptoms can show up as early as preschool years, so it is best to stay informed and alert for possible signs. If you feel unsure about what is going on with your child, you can always bring your child for a thorough assessment. Your child will thank you for your quick decision because it will save him or her from struggling later on.

Chapter II: Knowing When to Seek Help

Your preschooler will continuously surprise you, especially when he or she learns to speak and walk more. Just about every day, he or she will achieve new milestones. If somebody in your family has dyslexia, and/or if your child does not appear to be hitting the typical developmental milestones, then you have to seek help.

Your child cannot be diagnosed with dyslexia until the age of 8 because dyslexia is primarily a learning problem, so it cannot be detected much earlier. Evaluators can use several tests, including the Dyslexia Early Screening Test, on kids as young as four years old to look for weaknesses in learning skills. A child has to show several shortcomings in these skills to be considered at risk.

Delayed speech

Delayed speech is a sign of dyslexia. If your child is not speaking by age two or older, you will want to be more watchful of their reading progress when school starts. Delayed speech does not necessarily mean that your child has dyslexia, but it does alert you to look for more definitive signs. Even before school starts, you must have your child's hearing assessed, and you may want to talk to a speech therapist to ensure that your child's mouth and jaw muscles are well-developed.

If your child has unclear and muddled speech, then it is enough reason for you to keep an eye on his or her development. If they fumble and stutter for the words uttered and turn three, then contact your public school district immediately. You could get a free assessment and speech therapy before your child starts school and for the rest of the school life if he or she is entitled to free public education.

Here are a few more language issues that may show dyslexia:

>Receptive speech – Can your child understand what is being said to him without needing for it to be repeated several times? Does he or she show difficulty in differentiating "over" and "under," as well as "behind" and "in front?" Such confusion, especially with directional instructions, is another indicator of dyslexia.

>Word retrieval – Can your child slow to recall familiar objects? Dyslexics know what they wish to say but cannot pick it up from their minds.

>Stammering – This is the involuntary blockage of the usual speech patterns. While it is not linked to dyslexia, a child hesitating as he or she tries to find the words and stammers, then it could be a warning sign.

>Poor letter articulation – This is another possible warning sign, such as when your child says "gween and wed" instead of "green and red."

Ear infections

A big warning sign to watch out for in kids under five years old is recurring ear infections. They do not mean that your child has dyslexia, but many people with dyslexia have a history of ear infections. The infections do not cause dyslexia, but they may make the condition worse by impairing your child's hearing ability, especially at a time when progress in auditory processing is expected.

Experts agree that, while dyslexia is about hearing sounds, it is not a hearing impairment. A dyslexic child can hear sounds but processes them wrong. The condition is "phonemic" and not a hearing disorder. He or she cannot distinguish between phonemes in the same way that other kids do. A child who lacks phonemic awareness cannot differentiate words like top and tot, cut and cot, and Tim (name) and tin.

If you are worried about your child's hearing, then see a doctor right away. You may consult an audiologist for a hearing assessment and seek private help when it uncovers any issue. You can also take the test results to your school district, hoping to receive free support for as long as he or she needs it.

Vision problems

Your child's vision problem does not cause dyslexia, but can complicate it. Many dyslexics often complain of seeing fuzzy, wobbly, or moving letters. Your dyslexic child may have vision issues, but dyslexia is primarily a phonemic processing problem. Even when the letters are in focus for them, they will still have difficulty matching sounds to the letters.

Many vision problem symptoms are similar to that of dyslexia. You need the help of an expert to determine the proper diagnosis. Your child may have a vision issue if you notice that he is doing any of the following:

>Does not enjoy being read to
>Likes being read to, but does not show interest in letters and words
>Gets lost along the lines of print
>Has watery or strained eyes whenever he or she looks at books
>Complains of double, blurred, or moving print
>Frowns, squints, or rubs eyes while staring at books
>Holds book or tilts head too closely whenever looking at books
>Covers an eye to check a text
>Shows difficulty spotting alike and different items
>Evades close-up tasks
>Easily distracted
>Exhibits a short attention span
>Needs plenty of breaks from paper-and-pen activities
>Gets tired quickly when tracing or drawing
>Has difficulty tracing and copying letters and shapes
>Reverses numbers and letters
>Has poor self-confidence
>Often complains of headaches
>Shows poor hand-eye coordination
>Seems clumsy or awkward

The American Academy of Ophthalmology said children must have a complete eye exam when they reach four years old and routine eye exams every two years after that. You can consult a pediatric optometrist for these tests.

Issues with motor skills

Kids with dyslexia often have poor hand-eye coordination, as well as fine motor skills. Dyslexics have difficulty catching and throwing, and performing tasks like buttoning shirts, tying shoelaces, or threading beads. He or she may take a while to develop a dominant hand.

Plenty of children have poor hand-eye coordination and even experience being ambidextrous (being able to use both hands) at one time. These behaviors do not indicate that your child has dyslexia, but they are potential indicators. They do not indicate dyslexia unless they persist in school.

Pre-reading problems

Specific pre-reading issues can be potential dyslexia symptoms. If your child struggles with several pre-reading behaviors, right through grade one, and otherwise responsive and bright, ask for a thorough assessment.

Here are signs to watch out for:

>Your child cannot identify sounds inside the words.

>Your child cannot hear rhyming words.

>Your child does not show interest in words or letters.

>Your child cannot identify the letters from the squiggles.

>Your child cannot retell, even a simple story.

>Your child is not interested in hearing stories.

>Your child cannot recognize or write his or her name.

Activities that help build pre-reading skills:

There are plenty of language activities that you can prepare your child for reading, which can help build the following skills:

>Print awareness: When your child understands that the print goes from left to right, and top to the bottom, then he or she is primed for following the sentences in a text. Dyslexics require plenty of this skill because directional instructions can be tricky for them. When some kids begin school, they are clueless about holding a book or following the lines. Print awareness is developed by you merely reading to your child and pointing out the text's direction.

>Phonemic and phonics skills: Your child must first develop a few skills before he or she can read: phonemic awareness (or hearing sounds in the words), and phonics (or matching the letters to the sounds). You want your preschooler to do tons of rhyming, singing, and saying letter sounds to develop his or her phonemic awareness and form solid phonic skills. Your child must develop sequential skills that begin with phonemic awareness:

>>Phonemic awareness: Before giving your child any instruction in the letters, he or she must first be aware that the words are made of sounds.

>>Phonological awareness: It is about sounds, too, but this means that your child appreciates sounds more. He or she can identify chunks of sound, like rhymes and prefixes.

>>Phonics: Once your child is aware that words are made of sounds, he or she must discover that the chunks of letters and written letters represent those sounds.

>>Morphological and orthographic awareness: Words that are easy to sound out, such as pink and stamp, are the first in line when teaching phonemic and phonological awareness. Once your child becomes comfortable with them, he or she should be introduced to the harder words, including suffixes, prefixes, contractions, and more. Learning and mastering the suffixes and prefixes is called morphological awareness, where your child recognizes the parts of words that have meaning. On the other hand, orthographic awareness is about getting to know which letters come together and appear right.

Developing your child's phonemic awareness

Initially, your child is at the phonemic awareness stage. You need to help him or her hear the sounds that the words are made of. The following activities are great for helping your child develop phonemic awareness:

>Help him or her hear the sounds in rhymes and songs by leaving key words out whenever you sing them. Your child gives the words using the rhyme as a guide.

>Enjoy alliterations, and read rhyming stories.

Improving phonics skills

You will know that your child is ready to match letters and sounds when they get the idea that words have sounds and could come together in rhyming patterns. Help him or her remember the sounds and shapes of letters by making him or her get his or her hands on them. A dyslexic child can learn pretty well when you guide him or her in using all of the senses, and not just hearing and vision. Allow him or her to remember the sound that every letter makes by associating it to a character or object.

Getting ready for kindergarten

You want your child to be as ready as possible for kindergarten. If you notice him or her doing things, such as wandering off whenever you read him or her stories, then you want to ensure that his other skills are well developed. In a perfect world, your child emerges radiant and excited with newly acquired information after his or her first day at kindergarten.

If you feel that your child has dyslexia, you will want to look closely at his language skills. The teachers are hoping for the following skills, and a dyslexic student needs to work on at least three of them:

>Identifying the beginning sound of words
>Identifying some of the alphabet letters
>Recognizing the rhyming sounds
>Recognizing some common sight words, such as "stop"
>Recognizing his or her written name
>Telling a simple story

>Trying to write his or her name

Quick tips

Some dyslexic children struggle to recall sequences of directional concepts (like over and under), and numbers. Below you will see that these skills are prominently noticed in kindergarteners, which is why frequent practice before schooling is critical.

>Understanding general times of day: It is normal for kids to have difficulty determining the times of day, but this becomes even more confusing for dyslexic children.

>Understanding directions, such as in and out, up and down, over and behind, in front and behind, and left and right.

>Counting up to 10: Many kids could count up to ten as early as toddler years. By the time they start school, nearly every kid can manage to do it, and a dyslexic child may not.

>Tracing the basic shapes: Most small kids could trace shapes after learning to hold a pencil, while a dyslexic child usually draws off the shape.

>Recognizing shapes

>Naming colors

>Sorting items by size, shape, and color

>Identifying body parts

Dyslexia is NOT a behavioral disorder

Your child will not behave unusually or badly because of dyslexia. He or she might try to draw attention in other ways when he is infuriated, frustrated, or demoralized because of the condition. Your child's teacher hopes that all kids in his or her class have these basic social skills:

>The student uses words and not fists.
> The student speaks clearly.
> The student plays with other kids.
> The student follows simple directions.
> The student can tell what he or she wants and needs.
> The student waits for his or her turn.
> The student goes to the bathroom by himself or herself.
> The student is curious, and knows how to ask questions.
> The student loves hearing stories.
> The student says "please", and "thank you" when appropriate.

Monitoring your school-aged child

If the teacher tells you that your five-year-old child is not ready to read, then he or she may be right. However, if he or she says the same thing when your child is seven, and you see that your child shows confusion with words, then he or she is wrong. Only a few children learn to read much later than the others, but they are the ones who need help and not whose difficulties go farther and deeper.

Dyslexic kids do not suddenly "get" it, but they continue to struggle while the others overtake them. Their difficulty with text is noticeable at ages five to seven when almost all other kids are "getting it." The learning gap will only continue to grow without intervention.

Dyslexia does not get better on its own. You need to start treating it as early as possible, so things become easier and quicker for your child to make headway. The problems only compound when you delay the treatment. When you extend extra help to your child, the young ones will do best. After age 10, only 25 percent of dyslexic children catch up to their grade level.

Do not panic if your child is already 10 or older. It is never too late for a person to learn to read but practice more frequently and consistently. Your older child must work longer and harder than he or she would if she started at age five, but he or she can still obtain the same end.

Starting to feel unhappy and being disorganized

Your child knows he or she is at the bottom of the class, dreads doing homework, and dislikes going to school. What can you do about it? You can talk it over with your child. Allow him or her to know that you understand the humiliation that he or she currently feels because she cannot read like the others. Tell your child that you know that he or she tries hard, and that you are there to help. Pinpoint the difficulties together, and do writing and reading exercises to help lessen the burden, and get a thorough assessment for dyslexia.

You can tell your child about dyslexia, and the many famous personalities who have it. Dyslexic children almost always say that they feel inspired and empowered whenever they realize that talented and clever people have dyslexia.

If you notice that your child is disorganized, then the best way to help him or her with it is to forget about fighting it. He or she is unlikely to become organized instantly. Your child, however, can harness every help possible.

Talking to your child's teacher

You should talk about your child's dyslexia with his or her teacher so your child does not get classified instantly as not being developmentally-ready. It is easy to mistake the condition with more superficial reading issues. If you feel uncertain, then tell the teacher what you are thinking and the symptoms you have observed, so you are both on the same page.

You want your child's teacher to help you track your child's progress and be able to pinpoint the areas that need help. Ask the teacher about his or her observations, and ask to be shown the projects and test results of your child. Note down what he or she has to tell you, as well as what you ask for. The paper trail will be handy later on, and serve as a baseline, so make sure to glance at it as often as you can.

Having your child tested for dyslexia

One great reason for getting your child diagnosed is to know exactly what is going on, especially when you suspect that something is wrong. Here are more reasons to seek professional help and get an assessment:

>You get to know whether your child has dyslexia.
>You discover whether your child has other problems, such as dysgraphia (writing difficulty) and attention-deficit hyperactivity disorder (ADHD).
>You have a baseline from which to gauge his or her progress
>If your child has LD, then he or she receives special education.
>Test results allow your child's teacher to understand his or her struggles
>You get an insight into the best help that you can provide your child

When your child shows reading difficulties, you will often hear from other people to wait awhile. Most kids begin to read between five and seven years old, and make the fastest progress. If you see that your child's reading development is alarmingly slow, then act quickly. Your child will need extra help now.

Trust your instincts. If you feel that your child is falling behind, he or she is most likely, even if your teachers tell you that your child is doing fine. Up to age 10, a dyslexic child can still significantly improve when given good help. After that, things will become harder, but it is never too late.

Never too late

It is never too late to check whether your child has dyslexia. The testing process becomes easier when you are older. Older adults and children are articulate and experienced. They can show their dyslexia by providing a verbal account of their challenges. A psychologist may have to offer them only one or two tests.

Looking for a Test Administrator

You can get your child tested for possible dyslexia through the school psychologist, or an independent psychologist, or both.

Within your child's school district

The first person you need to approach when you wish to have your child assessed is the classroom teacher. You may ask the school psychologist for help right away, but he or she may endorse you to the teacher for an initial consultation. The test results from the psychologist will be the key to your school district's decision. You will then be asked to a meeting with the school, where you will be informed on the district's actions in response to the test results.

Pros: If your child is tested in school, then the service is free.
Cons: You do not get to choose who carries out these tests, and where the testing venue will be. You will also have no voice about the testing day.

Independent Test Administrators

A lot of people can test your child. Normally, only psychologist-given test results are accepted by the school districts. Insurance companies may also contribute to the testing cost, but only when given by a psychologist. Practitioners, who normally call themselves "consultants," "therapists," or "tutors," can give the assessment you need to design a program for your child, but they normally do not give a dyslexia assessment.

A "therapist" or "consultant" title means that the practitioner has more qualifications than a tutor. It may mean that the person is qualified, typically with a psychologist's certification, to give you a diagnosis that will be recognized by your school district. You want to ask a therapist or consultant about their qualifications and then run this past your school district to ensure you are talking to the right person.

However, not all practitioners use the medical term "dyslexia." Find somebody else if the practitioner that you are considering is not explicitly looking for the condition. How do you know whether you should get an independent tester?

Here are five great reasons to opt for an independent tester:

>The school district will not test your child. They feel that your child will not qualify for the extra help, and the money it would cost them to test him or her should go to the needier kids. However, it is unusual for the district to

reject your request for assessment because when your child is tested independently and results revealed he needs extra help, then the district can be legally put in a tricky spot.

>The district tells you it will test your child, but you do not want to wait long for it.

>The district has already tested your child, but you are not in complete agreement with the results and you want a second opinion.

>Your child feels embarrassed by his problems, and he does not want any special education and requests for the most low-key help.

>You see the importance of controlling over the test administrator, as well as when and where it is given. You want confidentiality, and you may not want the district to know about the results.

The downside of independent testing is that you have to pay for the service.

Test results and the terminologies

When the test administrator shows you the test results, you are bound to hear some words that you may not be familiar with. Here are some of the common terminologies that you will likely hear:

>Age: A test age of 7.2 means the performance shown is like that of an average child, aged seven years and two months.

>Auditory access: This is about pulling out sound information, such as parts of words and names of things, from the mind. It is often measured by asking a child to name pictures quickly. If your child cannot quickly tell everyday objects, such as a toothbrush, then he or she has weak auditory access.

>Auditory memory: This is about keeping some sound-information in mind for a short time. It is often measured by asking the child to recall a few words over a few minutes. If they cannot remember a sequence of numbers right after being told and asked to remember them, they have weak auditory memory.

>Percentile ranking: If your child receives a percentile ranking of 14, then it means that he or she is in the bottom 14 out of 100 average children.

>Phonemic skills: This has to do with the phonemes. Your child's phonemic skills are tested when he or she is asked what sounds they hear inside the words.

>Phonologic skills: This refers to the general letter, sound, and word skills. If your child can differentiate the sounds inside the words, and the words that sound alike, they have good phonologic skills.

>Standardized: A standardized test is given to hundreds of students to allow the test administrator to create a standard bell curve of scores to plot your child's test scores. The administrator will know how kids generally perform on this test and compare your child's scores to the general population.

Section 504

Your child, once diagnosed as having an LD, will get special education. His or her rights can be found in the Individuals with Disabilities Education Act (IDEA). If your child does not qualify as having an LD, then another legal safety net may apply, which is called Section 504 of the Rehabilitation Act of 1973. It is for kids with ADHD and other similar conditions that do not count as learning disabilities.

Section 504 states that schools should make reasonable accommodations for kids with "functional impairment" that substantially limit major life activity. Furthermore, the act says that schools must have a Section 504 official. You can ask your school to give you a parents' rights manual, and set an appointment with an official. Your child should receive assistance, such as having test questions read aloud instead of having to read them himself or herself.

Independent tutor

If your child struggles in class, then you may want to hire a private tutor whether or not he or she receives extra help in school. When you look for a learning center or tutor, consider the following:

>The travel distance
>The cost of the lessons
>The tutor's experience and qualifications
>Whether the tutor provides phonological, structured, and sequential instruction

>Whether you could sell the idea to your child

No matter what happens, you can opt to help your child at home. Never think that, just because you are a dyslexic-trained instructor, you can no longer be effective. Homeschooling is becoming increasingly popular and may even be an option for you.

Deciding not to test

Most people get the tests done because they wish to know what is going on, and how they can move forward. The tests provide a starting point to gauge the progress. However, you may decide to do without the testing after considering all the factors (like the LD label, the anxiety, and the likelihood of not getting special education).

It would be best if you only skipped testing when your child's problems appear mild and after you have had a discussion with the school teacher. The solution for dyslexia is determined through the tests. If you have any doubts on what you can and should do, then get your child tested.

The following gives you reasons why not testing may be an option for you:

>You cannot afford it. While big and comprehensive tests are recommended, so are small and quick tests.

>You feel that your child's school teacher goes the extra mile for him or her, despite not being formally considered as having an LD.

>You know a great tutor and believe that he or she will help your child progress.

>You have done your homework and joined the IDA in your area. You understand that your child needs a lot of practice, and you are helping him or her yourself or are getting a tutor.

Chapter III: Exploring Your Options

Your child needs ample support to overcome dyslexia. He or she will need to mix with people who truly understand her situation and will not bring him or her down. Your child may even have unique talents that need to be nurtured, too. Before making that big move and decide which school to send him or her to, here are questions that you need to have answered:

>How many students are in a class?
>Are the teachers sensitive to all the children's needs?
>What kind of support will your child receive with reading?
>Does the school use reading programs, such as Orton-Gillingham?
>How much group work will the students do?
>How much homework will your child receive?
>Does the school have a homework club?
>Can your child use a computer for most assignments?
>Does your child's prospective teacher promote a classroom-buddy system?
>What extracurricular activities are being offered by the school?
>Does your child have friends in the local public school?
>Is there parent-involvement in the school programs?
>Does the school encourage you to help in class and let you drop in anytime?
>Does the school have a tutoring program?
>Does your local public school have a good resource teacher?
>Is your local public school well-equipped with things, such as new computers and books?

>Are the teachers at the local public school happy and friendly to the students?
>Is the principal at the local public school approachable?
>Will the local public school, welcome your visits?
>Is there a local charter school in the area?
>Are the other schools within convenient traveling distance for us?
>Do you have special requirements, such as wanting a Catholic education for your child or advanced instruction in violin?
>Can you afford private school?
>Can you afford to send your child to a private tutor or consultant as an alternative to public education?

After prioritizing your questions, you and your dyslexic child must visit the local public school to see whether they offer the things you want. You should also phone the school to set an appointment and keep your child in the loop to ensure he or she is mentally prepared. Try to see the classes in session, and check the places that will be socially important to your child, such as the cafeteria and the lockers. You should get a feel of what the school is like, and what they can do for your child.

Traditional public schools

Your local public school should extend extra help, as long as you can show them that your child needs it.

Assessments

The good thing about approaching your local public school is that you can get a free dyslexia assessment. All you have to do is to file a written request with the school district, and a reply is normally sent in 30 days. An educational psychologist will run a battery of tests, and your child will receive special education if found to have dyslexia or a learning disability.

You will probably hear about your child's special learning disability or learning disability, rather than her dyslexia. Dyslexia is a learning disability, but the teachers do not often use the term because they do not feel qualified to do so. The school psychologist may not use it, either, since his or her mandate is to deal with learning disabilities.

Your child may have dyslexia but is still unqualified for special education. He or she may be struggling, but not enough to qualify for special education. If you are solely dependent on the school's special education program in this instance, then you do not receive it until your child's condition worsens enough to reach the required performance level.

School programs

If you are new to special education, you want to familiarize yourself with the popular programs. Most of the programs below are predominantly used in public schools but may also be used in learning centers and private schools.

>Orton-Gillingham (O-G):

The O-G was developed by Anna Gillingham and Samuel Orton in the 1930s. This is called the grandfather of phonics, multisensory, and research-based programs. It engages your child's senses as he or she learns phonics patterns and rules. It is the most popular program of this bunch, and plenty of tutors and teachers are trained in O-G. You can even train yourself, too. Just visit www.ortonacademy.org or call 845-373-8919.

>Lindamood-Bell:

This is a group of programs designed by Bell and Lindamood, with the most widely used being the Lindamood Intensive Phonological Sequencing (LIPS). This particular program makes kids aware of their mouths' actions whenever they utter different sounds. The Lindamood-Bell programs are short but intense as your child receives one-on-one help for four to six weeks, four hours per day. For info, visit www.lblp.com or call 800-233-1819.

>Project Read:

Project Read is the most frequently used program in schools. There are five curriculum strands involved: phonology, written expression, linguistics, and two kinds of reading comprehension. It can be used in special and regular classes, and with all ages. For info, visit www.projectread.com or call 800-450-0343.

>Spalding:

This is an adaptation of the O-G, but with emphasis on writing. The program is used in learning centers and schools in many countries. An online parent course shall be available soon, too. For info, visit www.spalding.org or call 602-866-7801.

>Slingerland:

This program is created for classrooms. There are summer programs being offered, too. Kids learn the phonetic sounds, and do plenty of writing. For info, visit www.slingerland.org or call 425-453-1190.

>Corrective Reading:

SRA, which now joined with McGraw-Hill, produces learning kits and programs. The company has been around for decades. One of its programs, Corrective Reading, is one of the most frequently mentioned in schools and learning centers. The program involves the teacher reading out instructions from the manual to a group of students, and the students must read and answer their workbooks at the same time. For info, visit www.sraonline.com or call 888-772-4543.

>LANGUAGE!:

This program is created for middle- and high school students partly because it incorporates all the 18 language arts and reading curriculum strands. It is used in some learning centers, as well. For info and materials, visit www.language-usa.net or call 800-547-6747, ext. 266.

>Reading Recovery:

The program originated in New Zealand, but it has spread to learning centers and schools worldwide. It is designed for children in grade 1 and involves intensive daily instruction for 12 to 20 weeks. It gives children individual instruction and plenty of reading at their level. For info, visit www.reading recovery.com or call 614-310-7323.

>Read Naturally:

This program helps improve your child's reading fluency and is used by schools, learning centers, and therapists. Your child repeats readings of short text pieces. He or she will read the text out loud, while listening to it on recorded audio. The reading speed is timed for every separate reading. For the bigger picture on reading Naturally, go to www.readnaturally.com.

>Wilson:

Teachers show students how they tap out the sounds in the words and improve their memory. It was initially designed for older students, but it now has materials available for younger children. For info, visit www.wilsonlanguage.com or call 800-782-3766.

>Lexia Herman Method (also called Herman Method):

This program requires students to complete 21 instruction levels. Each instruction has handwriting and spelling components. The instruction is phonics- and multisensory-based, with emphasis on comprehension. For more information, go to www.hermanmethod.com.

>Success for All (SFA):

This is a school-based program to help at-risk or disadvantaged children in pre-K to grade 6 read better. Schools that use this program receive support from the

Success for All Foundation funded by donations. The organization also produces other learning programs, such as Kinder Corner and Curiosity Corner for little kids and the Reading Edge for adolescents. For info, check out www.successforall.net.

>Davis Learning Strategies:

The Gift of Dyslexia author Ron Davis, who is dyslexic himself, has created Davis Learning Strategies, where you can bring your child for an assessment and tutoring. Teachers can also attend workshops and buy the Davis boxes for struggling readers. For info, check out at www.davislearn.com.

>Early Intervention in Reading:

This is used only in schools. It also offers an easy and inexpensive way to provide regular teachers training in giving struggling readers explicit phonics instruction and the guided reading they need. Teachers receive online-based training and learn how to provide struggling kids 20 minutes of daily instruction in a group of up to seven students per class. For more info, visit www.earlyinterventioninreading.com.

Remember – Just because a program has a proven track record does mean that your child will succeed in it. If your child hates your chosen program, do not think that you have come to a dead end. Look for another teacher or program with experience with struggling kids.

You can also introduce phonetic and multisensory activities to your child and see how he or she fares. You do not need a Ph.D. to see whether your child enjoys tutoring, getting used to sounding out, and becoming a better reader.

Help beyond the classroom

Public schools could do incredible things for your dyslexic child outside of the class. When teachers and parents work together, all kinds of things can happen. Here are some of the activities and clubs that you may want to ask about in a school:

>Buddy system: Your child can be a buddy for a younger child or be taken under an older child's wing himself or herself.

>Homework club: If your school has a homework club, then it could be worth your time to check it out. Older kids often help out in such clubs, and you may just find a child who can take special care of your child.

>Special responsibilities: Good teachers know that providing a special student responsibilities, such as being a litter patroller or lunch monitor, works wonders for a child's self-confidence.

>Specialty one-off programs: Sometimes, schools offer a short program to help kids with things, such as assertiveness.

>Sports and arts: Encourage your child to join in any non-academic activities that he or she enjoys. Happy kids are better equipped to withstand the struggles that dyslexia can bring.

>Tutoring for your child: Most schools are parents to listen to kids reading. They often set up programs where a parent works with a child once or twice per week. Once a volunteer parent realizes how to help your child, significant progress can come from this one-on-one coaching.

>Your child tutoring other children: It may seem ridiculous, but it works. When the teacher finds something that your child can cope with, such as marking spellings from answer sheets, your child can feel important and useful. It also brushes up their skills in the process.

Meeting the school staff

A good teacher for dyslexic children will fit small group activities into the programs, encourages creativity, matches up buddies, and maintains a warm but disciplined atmosphere in the room. He or she has unique skills, too, because your child has a few special needs. A good teacher for your child is also:

>Approachable: Your child can always go to him or her after class and seek extra guidance.
>Flexible: If one strategy does not work, then he or she will be willing to try another.
>Aware: He or she understands that when your child cannot do things in the same way as the other children, it does not mean she cannot do them at all. Your child should not be allowed to skip tasks. He or she needs to try out different strategies until he or she finds what fits.

Requesting a teacher for your child

Teachers get together at the beginning and/or end of the school year to see which child goes with which teacher. The principal oversees the whole process. While it seems unfair that you do not get to choose your child's teacher, here are some things that you can do to raise your odds of getting your child a good teacher:

>Fill out the optional information sheet that you receive at the end of every school year. You should not say things like, "I do not want the short-tempered and boring Ms. Sarah." Instead, you can say things like, "my child responds best to gentle discipline," and then hope for the best.

>Talk to the teacher you would like your child to have.

>When the new school year starts, you should go to the principal's office right away if you do not like the teacher. If you raise a good point, then the principal may place your child into another class. If you wait too long before approaching the principal, then you will likely be told that it is too late.

>Be friendly with your child's current teacher, so you can politely ask him or her to place your child with a specific teacher next school year.

>If your child receives special education, then talk to his or her resource teacher. Let him or her know which teacher you would like for your child, so he or she can add comments to the selection process.

>If your child hates going to school, and you do not know whether to file a complaint or sit the bad year out, always remember that your child can seriously fall behind in the early years. Document all the incidents, as well as comments that your child tells you about, and date every report. Bring the record to the principal, and then request for a change of class.

Your child's reading difficulties do not get better by themselves. Without intervention, the problems will get worse. If your child does not receive good intervention or is unhappy in her class (despite getting help from a resource teacher), then speak up. Trust your judgment, and never wait for somebody to give you the go signal. If your child has become unhappy, then taking immediate action does not mean that you are overreacting. You should be making it a priority.

Getting to know the resource teacher

Public schools usually have a resource teacher responsible for ensuring your child's Individualized Education Program runs productively and smoothly. Typically, your child goes to the resource room a few times a week to receive small group instruction with the resource teacher. It is up to your school to decide what your child gets, which is influenced by staffing and budget.

Plenty of good resource teachers use their mix of strategies instead of a commercial program. They understand how important phonemic awareness is for your child. Teachers are frequently under a lot of pressure to train children in new programs, but you still cannot beat empathy, experience, and an open and lively mind. You should be able to spot these qualities by talking to a resource teacher and observing their classroom.

Resource teachers, as well as special education teachers, give special education to students entitled to it. If your school has both kinds of teachers, then the resource teacher normally works with more moderately-disabled students and may even teach gifted children. He or she is often trained in reading programs, such as the Orton-Gillingham, while special education teachers have training in stuff, including wheelchair-bound kids into the normal student life.

The support staff

You probably almost have as much contact with the school secretary as you do with the teachers. You speak to the secretary each time you make an appointment to meet the speech therapist, school psychologist, or other specialists. This is also the case when your child forgets his or her lunch, has an outside appointment, or stays home sick. If you are nice to this person, then your life will run smoother.

You may, however, encounter an officious secretary or two. When dealing with such people, you are in the midst of real power. Make sure to tread warily. Do not forget the janitor, too, because he can let your child in after-hours when nobody else can. These people will be beneficial, as long as your child is going to school.

The principal

You may have a lot of contact with the school principal, especially if he or she has a special interest in kids with special needs. He or she may even talk to you about your initial concerns, as well as attend subsequent IEP meeting, even though he or she does not have to. You often deal almost exclusively with teachers, and meetings that include the principal may mean a problem that has not been resolved.

Meeting the principal and getting friendly with him or her becomes easy when your child is in a small school. However, in a big middle- or high school, things become much harder when dealing with the principal. He or she becomes harder to track down and meets you only when you have serious concerns. It will still come in handy when you have the principal's contact details written down, just in case.

Alternative schooling

If you think that your child will not receive any help that they need in your local public school or have other reasons for wanting to keep your out of the public school system, you have a few options. You can either choose from schools run by their own set of beliefs, those that cater to people with dyslexia, or those that meet your religious needs.

You are entitled to tax deductions for your child's specialized schooling and tutoring, as long as you can present that a doctor recommended it. Your expenses will be treated as medical, and you can only deduct amounts that exceed 7.5 percent of your adjusted gross income. You may read the IRS Publication 502 (Medical and Dental Expenses), which you can download from www.irs.gov/publications/p502/

Charter schools

A charter school is a free public school, but with more self-regulation than a regular public school. It writes its own charter but must comply with some of the district's guidelines. Even though it is state-funded, teachers and parents are free to choose curriculums and methods. Over 41 states have charter schools. If you are in one of these states, then you are eligible to enroll your child.

Here are a few more things that you need to know about charter schools:

>A child-centered, less formal curriculum
>A cooperative setup, where parents must volunteer in class or in ways that help the school for a specific number of hours per semester
>Community involvement
>Innovative new teaching methods

Magnet schools

A magnet school is another type of public school that you may want to consider. This school initially began as a way to help schools desegregate, offering attractive options to black students. Each magnet school has a particular focus, such as preparing students for military, scientific, or musical careers.

If your dyslexic child has his or her heart set on a career path, then you can see what every magnet school in your country offers. You can also check for requirements by checking out the Magnet Schools of America website (www.magnet.edu). You will probably also want to include private tutoring in your plan because magnet schools do not usually offer specialized treatments for dyslexia.

Private school

Waldorf schools, Montessori schools, and schools for people with dyslexia are considered private. Private schools include single-gender schools and religious schools. They are not governed by the same laws covering public schools and do not have to give special education to children with learning disabilities. You have to ask the school what kind of help they can offer your child.

You will also need to understand that, whatever help your child does or does not get, you cannot press your rights under the Individuals with Disabilities Education Act (IDEA). If you do not want your child to go to a private school full time or cannot afford it, ask about summer school. A lot of schools offer summer classes, and they usually are popular, so enroll early.

Montessori schools

Montessori schools started in the early 1900s. This type of private school was introduced by Italian educator and physicist Maria Montessori. You can now find many

Montessori schools across the globe. Here are the key features that you need to note:

>Classes have 20 to 30 students and two or three teachers.
>Students in each class are mixed ages and begin at age 2.
>The alphabet and sounds are introduced to students at age 2, with materials like sandpaper cutouts and letter blocks.
>All kids do a lot of hands-on activities.
>Teachers watch over the students and provide new materials when they seem ready.
>Teachers introduce kids to specific stimuli, such as music and dance, when they are thought to be at the most receptive age.
>Your child will learn as an individual and only begin doing group work in high school.
>Classes are clean, quiet, and orderly, with emphasis on responsibility and self-care.

Montessori schools introduce your child to phonetics at an early age. They also use non-competitive and multisensory strategies. The only downside is that your child may not master reading during the early years and may need specialized tutoring.

Deciding on a school

Many private schools specifically cater to children with dyslexia. Some of them are even boarding schools. They have websites and brochures that you can browse. The big advantage of these schools is that kids like them will surround your child, and all teachers are focused on teaching your child in a dyslexia-friendly manner.

The factors that may shock you are geographic and financial. You have to pay for these schools and may have to travel a long way to bring your child there every day. Before getting into these issues, you have homework to do. Every school is different, which is why you need to get a feel for each one. You can check www.ldresources.org for a list of K to 12 schools.

Home schooling

Homeschooling is an option that you may want to consider. There are many places to turn to for help as you plan curriculums. Furthermore, homeschooling may even be cheaper for you than private tutoring or schooling. Here are a few more things to ponder:

>Home schooling can appear cheaper than sending your dyslexic child to private school.
>You do not have to travel long distances every day to send your child to private school.
>Plenty of homeschooling curriculums, support groups, and online courses are available everywhere. Parents of dyslexic children say that choosing curriculums is the most significant advantage of homeschooling. They can find materials that fit their child instead of pushing him or her through a one-size-fits-all system.
>Home-schooled children generally do well in tests than publicly-schooled kids.
>Home schooling lets you respond to your child's academic needs while protecting her emotional health.

>You can always send back your child to the public school system.

Homeschooling parents believe that, as long as you are reasonably level-headed and can get along well with your child without many showdowns, then you may be surprised by how stress-free the process becomes. Of course, you can make your discoveries on fun lessons. You can also use desired multisensory techniques to teach your child phonemic awareness.

Reading textbooks

With so many reading books to choose from, pick attractive books with well-spaced text comfortably spread throughout the pages for your dyslexic child. Most words must sound out regularly, and it is helpful if the new and tricky words are given in a separate list that your child can check. You may also want to focus on book series, so your child can read several books before searching anew.

Here are some great examples:

>The Alphabet Series: There are two volumes in this series. At the back of each book, you will see questions to ask your child and the sight words he or she should learn, so flip to these first. The books, published by Educators Publishing Service, are available at www.epsbooks.com.

>Reading Rainbow Readers: Each book in the series is comprised of themed short stories. The books are published by SeaStar Books and can be purchased at all bookstores.

>Real Kids Readers: This series has three levels. The text is phonetically-controlled, and the photos appear real. The books also appeal to a wide age range. They are published by Millbrook Press, and are available at all bookstores.

>Bob Books: There are 12 small books per box. The boxes come in Levels A, B, and C, and there is more than one box per level. These are great for all kids as they are phonetically-leveled and cartoon characters illustrated are of indiscriminate age. They are published by Scholastic and can be purchased at all bookstores.

>Dr. Seuss: Hop on Pop, Green Eggs and Ham, and Cat in the Hay are the easiest books in this series. Published by Random House, all books are available at most bookstores.

>Primary Phonics: You get five sets of readers in this series with ten books for each set. The text is phonetically-controlled, and the illustrations are appealing to a broad readership. You may also purchase the workbooks separately. Published by the Educators Publishing Service, you can buy Primary Phonics at www.epsbooks.com.

Looking for workbooks

Workbooks can be handy when you and your child are just starting with homeschooling. You need books with simple instructions, and a gradual progression of phonics activities, such as:

>Building Spelling Skills: This includes a set of six workbooks. The series is available for grades 1 to 6. There are simple, repetitive lessons that focus on different words. Published by Evan-Moor, you can purchase this series at www.evan-moor.com.

>Explode the Code: This series includes over 17 books. These books, published by Educators Publishing Service, and written by Rena Price and Nancy Hall, can be purchased at www.epsbooks.com or by calling 800-225-5750.

>Reading Freedom (Activity Books 1 and 2): These books are easy to get online. Published by Pascal press of Australia, and written by Hunter Calder, you can buy these books at www.pascalpress.com.au.

>Reading Reflex: This book will tell you how to teach phonographix to your child. There are instructions for making letter cards and letting your child slide them together to form words. It also teaches you to create word games, and read short stories. Authored by Geoffrey and Carmen McGuinnes, and published by Free Press, this book is available at all bookstores.

>Recipe for Reading: This program is for kids in grades K to 6. It comprised of a teacher's manual, storybooks, workbooks, and other learning materials. Published by Educators Publishing Service and authored by Frances Bloom, Nina Traub, et al., you can buy these books at www.epsbooks.com or by calling 800-225-5750.

>See Johnny Read!: This book is for parents of young boys who struggle with reading. You are asked to give your child 20 to 40 minutes of daily reading and a one

hour lesson with him or her once or twice a week. Authored by Tracey Wood, and published by McGraw-Hill, the book is available in all bookstores, including online.

>Teach Your Child to Read in 100 Easy Lessons: This book gives you a step by step process to teaching your child the basics. It is an excellent pick for beginners. Authored by Siegfried Engelmann, et al., and published by Fireside, you can purchase it in all bookstores, including online.

>Toe by Toe: This is a manual and workbook in one. You will get progress charts and exercises. You will also be asked to tutor your child for 20 minutes daily. Your child must pass a mastery test before progressing to the next lesson. Authored by Keda and Harry Cowling, and published by Keda Publications, you can buy these books at www.toe-by-toe.co.uk.

Extra materials

Here are inexpensive and portable materials that you may want to have as you teach your dyslexic child:

>Lowercase letter cards: Check out letter blocks or letter cards at Creative Teaching Press. Affordable sets are available at the school suppliers store or online at www.creativeteaching.com.

>Book-sized whiteboards: You can simply buy a whiteboard and let your child write words. You can even play word games together.

>Flashcards: These can help your child practice patterns and phonics that he or she already learned. You can buy them from school supply stores or online.

Individualized Education Program

The Individualized Education Program is a detailed plan of how special education will be extended to your dyslexic child. Public schools are legally obliged to give disabled children with special education, as well as an IEP. On the other hand, private schools are not required to give special education or an IEP because they are free to make their own decisions on whether to provide for students with disabilities.

IEP meeting

It is a must that an IEP meeting takes place within 30 days after your dyslexic child is found to be eligible for special education. The school must provide notice for the meeting place and time. It is best to schedule it with both parents present. However, a friend or family member who knows your child's education and history will suffice if one cannot attend the meeting.

Never skip an IEP meeting. You do not get that many meetings, so treat each one with extreme importance. Talk to all involved parties, and make sure that your voice is heard and well-documented. The meeting people typically include you and/or your partner, the classroom teacher, a school district person for money allocation, the resource teacher, and a district person who will help simplify things for you.

Your child may also attend the meeting. He or she can speak up and be clear about his or her own goals. You can prepare your child ahead of time through role-playing. Children under seven years old may not benefit much from the meeting because it is difficult for them to fine their ideas and problems.

IEP document: The fine print

The IEP is a document that contains things like who does what, how, and when. It holds involved individuals responsible for their actions within the given time frame. The IEP must show your child's unique needs, present performance, and the practical and specific ways in which the school will meet these needs. The document also includes the following:

>Baseline: The IEP begins with an appraisal of your child's educational level to form a baseline from which to chart his or her progress. Members of the team will share test and observational data about your child to ensure everything is clear about his or her strengths and limitations.

>Goals: The team will outline short-term and long-term goals for your child, as well as benchmarks to watch for. These goals are specific and measurable.

>Ongoing evaluation: The team will tell you how the school will keep you updated about your child's progress. You can expect regular updates and can even ask for a meeting at any time when you notice that your child lacks progress.

>Accommodations: The team explains the special education accommodations and services provided to address your child's needs and goals. It also describes the details of the services, including frequency, date, and location. You can always ask for changes to the amount and type of special education that your child receives, the number and type of goals set for him or her, and the amount and type of other services he or she is getting.

>Transitioning: Transitioning is when your child progresses to a higher level. The team must prepare your child for it.

Preparing for the IEP meeting

Many parents read up and familiarize themselves with the IEP meeting. Some even take whole courses to be able to represent their child correctly. Below is the information that you need before heading to an IEP meeting:

>Speak to your child's teacher:

Before the IEP meeting, you want to talk to your child's teacher and ask these questions:
>>Who will attend the meeting
>>What will be discussed?
>>How is your child coping in every subject?
>>How well is your child in concentrating, following instructions, completing tasks, and organizing his or her work?

You will also want to tell the teacher what you want to bring up at the meeting so that you can develop some form of alliance with him or her.

>Make a list and organize all documents

List down the things that you want to discuss, such as:
>Specific things you want to ask and tell the team
>What you expect your child to learn this year, particularly in reading and writing
>Your child's strengths and weaknesses
>Strategies that you know have helped your child
>Your expectations when your child leaves school

>Find support

Ask a trusted friend or family member to go with you to the meeting. Make sure to let the school know in advance. You can also have an experienced advocate to accompany you.

Acts governing the IEP

The primary law governing special education and how the IEPs and assessments must be run is the Individuals with Disabilities Education Act (IDEA). The first IDEA was passed in the '90s, but it was updated in December 2004. The currect law, the Individuals with Disabilities Education Improvement Act, regulates everything connected with special education. This includes how the states receive federal funding to provide education to disabled children and what an IEP must include.

Each state has its own laws, and every district sees state and federal law has its ways. Stay in touch with the big organizations because their employees check out court cases and law amendments. Suppose your child is qualified to receive special education. In that case, they are eligible for protection under the Americans with Disabilities Act of 1990, and Section 504 of the Rehabilitation Act of 1973.

>Section 504 of the Rehabilitation Act: This civil rights law will protect disabled people in federally-funded services or programs. It requires schools to give free and appropriate education to disabled children. You will also find the due process you can go through should you have a serious complaint about your IEP team.

>ADA: This law protects those with a physical or mental impairment that limits substantially one or more life activities. It applies to the workplaces more than the schools, but it can add force to a case. The ADA can be handy for parents of kids in private schools, specifically the nonsectarian ones.

Knowing your and your child's rights

You can still feel shortchanged by the things applied through the IEP. It will help to ask a trained advocate or consider receiving training yourself. It will allow you to negotiate with the team and gain a better chance of obtaining what you want.

>Your child is entitled to get a free, appropriate, as well as inclusive education. However, you are not legally-entitled to ask for the "best" education for your dyslexic child.

>You are entitled to check and receive copies of the school records. You can also ask for an IEP meeting every year and review meetings in between. You must obtain progress reports at least as often as possible to get regular school reports.

>You have the right to due process. It means that you can get your case heard by an independent officer should you want to contest something or even ask for extra.

Securing help without IEP

An IEP is a working plan of how special education is given to an eligible child. While not every child qualifies for one, extra help can still be obtained under Section 504.

Choices in school

If your child is struggling in school, and you think he or she has dyslexia but did not qualify for special education and an IEP, then you still have options. You can ease your child's progress through school in various ways, including:
>Being nice to the teacher, and keep in contact with him or her.
>Attending parent-teacher conferences that come only two to three times a year.
>Finding where the problem lies when your child cannot do his or her homework.
>Keeping your ears and eyes alert for special extracurricular programs offering in school.

Help outside school

You have likely used private services for your child, or at least considered them. Getting outside help could take a huge amount of weight off your shoulders. It could also make gigantic hole in your pocket and leave you feeling discouraged.

>Specialized therapies:

Some dyslexia programs target the underlying cause instead of the symptomatic writing and reading issues. These programs include:
>>All Kinds of Minds: It shows your child how to use his or her best learning style.
>>Fast ForWord: Your child will learn how to listen better and respond faster.
>>Processing and Cognitive Enhancement (PACE): It runs your child through brain exercises.

>Dyslexia clinics:

A local dyslexia clinic could be another option for aiding your child's education in school. Dyslexia Institutes of America clinics offer a multisensory phonics-based reading program and treat related problems like phonemic awareness, poor working memory, visual perception, and more. Your child starts by having a screening test to see whether he or she has dyslexia, followed by a battery of tests to pinpoint the areas of weaknesses. The results determine what goes into your child's personalized treatment plan.

Your child gets two-hour sessions every week with certified teachers. The reading component will be taught one on one, and the sessions are followed up with home exercises that the parents are trained to do. Parents will also get weekly progress reports and another assessment every six months. The clinic director attends a parent-teacher meeting at school to keep teachers in the loop.

>Individual tutor:

You may find it hard to look for a tutor, particularly one who has taught a dyslexic child. Even though your prospective tutor looks good on paper, you still cannot be sure that your child will click with him or her. You want a tutor who:

>>Is nice: This is something you must look for, especially if you would like your child to go the extra mile with the help of a tutor.

>>Is relatable: Your child must relate to him or her and want to please him or her. The relationship will result in perseverance, and your child can get better marks in school.

>> An experienced and well-trained special education teacher is excellent in teaching reading: The teacher must have a teaching degree and a minimum of three years of teaching experience.

>>Knows about phonics-based and multisensory methods.

>>Can measure tests and show you the progress of your child after a few weeks of tutoring: You must remember, however, that your child may take a while to make

progress. You should see confidence, gradually building up in your child within weeks.

>>Is within your price range: Tutoring can cost a lot of money, s pick one who has all the qualities above but falls within your budget range.

Recommendations from trusted friends are great if you can get them.

>Learning centers

A learning center may offer more flexibility rather than an individual tutor. Your child may be able to go there at different times and may enjoy seeing other tutors. The downside is that tutors in learning centers are generally not qualified in special needs and do not have training in reading methods like Orton-Gillingham. They may also not know much about dyslexia.

>Academic support at home

Your child may seem like he or she hears half of what you say and then goes along with about a tiny fraction of that. However, without realizing it, your child absorbs your beliefs and habits. If you think that your child is having difficulty in school, you can help them.

>>Helping with homework:

Do what is best for your child by extending practical help that will gradually lead to independence. Each time you help your child, think about how you can take a supporting, instead of a leading role.

>>Using technology for help:

Kids who surf the Internet and confidently tap on the keyboard have a huge advantage over those who do not. You can use tools such as word processing programs, pocket spell checkers, books on tape, tape recorders, print-recognition software, and speech recognition programs.

>>Preventing math meltdown:

Primarily, dyslexia is a language disability. It can, however, have an impact on your child's math performance. He or she may have trouble recalling the sequences of numbers and what specialized words – like "reciprocal" and "product" – mean. Furthermore, your child may confuse written symbols and struggle with word problems.

Introduce simple math concepts. Use beans, counters, or coins to help your child see the four mathematical functions (addition, subtraction, multiplication, and division) in action. Bring those fractions to like by slicing up the cake, fruit, or bread. Show how your child can work out the area of your floor, and see small angles by making him or her open a door and tell whether he or she made a smaller or bigger angle.

Explain the place value with dimes and pennies. Help your child maintain a home bankbook with withdrawal and deposit columns, and figure out the running balance. Read the question at least twice, highlight the keywords, and draw a table for word problems. You can also try working on the word problem backward or making a guess and verifying it.

Avoiding the land mines

Some things that generally happen in school are virtual land mines for dyslexic children. Your child dreads taking tests and being graded, hates being timed, and cannot churn out figures and facts.

Fear of being graded

Your child may receive Cs, Ds, or worse, no matter how hard he or she tries because grades reflect a student's ranking rather than the efforts being made. You can ask for special consideration for your dyslexic child, and this is where the friendship you have built with the teacher comes in handy.

Ask the teacher to tweak his or her usual grading system to meet your child's needs. It is the kind of tweaking that places your child's effort into the picture. You may also want to collaborate with the teacher and list down identifiers that affect your child's grade.

Standardized tests are hard on your dyslexic child for many reasons:

>Your child may show difficulty reading the questions
>Your child may require more time than the other kids to answer the questions
>Your child may mark the wrong answer in multiple-choice tests because he or she confuses b and d
>Your child may be showing improvement in class, but results do not show that

>Your child may perform poorly on tests because he or she is nervous.

How can you help your child get through the tests and stay optimistic?

>Use your child's IEP to plan for the tests.

>The International Dyslexia Association and the Learning Disabilities Association have contested school district decisions. Make sure to consult the standard chain of command in your school before getting into the battle because they most likely do not want to get into a dispute with you.

You can also provide some help at home. Ask the resource teacher or guidance counselor about summer classes or whether they have practice tests that you can use. Your child needs plenty of practice runs on these tests. Approach them in short blasts, and make sure to have good things to eat. Keep in mind that you are preparing your child and not terrifying or exhausting him.

Retention

Many teachers and parents think that retention allows a child to mature and receive extra practice in class. However, studies show that retained kids:

>Feel ashamed in front of other kids because they are older and bigger than their classmates.
>Get teased by other kids for being "dumb."

>Feel that their parents misled or forced them into staying back a grade.
>Often fall back even further compared to other struggling kids who were never retained
>Are more likely to drop out of school than non-retained children.
>Often say that being retained was the worst thing that happened to them.

Holding your child a grade back can have long-term dangers.

At the time of transferring from one school to the next, grade retention may work for your dyslexic child. The lower grade may be more convincing for your child if he or she chooses it himself. Your child's teacher has a say in whether your child is promoted or retained. If you disagree with the proposed retention, despite your child's low test scores, then you must contest it and explain why your child must be promoted. There are no hard-and-fast retention rules, and some parents who have brought their objection to court have succeeded in getting their children promoted.

Rote learning

Rote learning allows your child to learn isolated facts by parroting them out plenty of times. These facts include dates of events, multiplication tables, and names of cities. Not many people do great with this type of learning because it is challenging to remember thing without using the memory joggers or attaching meaning to them. Your dyslexic child, however, may find this even harder as his or her short-term information recall is weak, even with memory joggers.

Your child can have significant stress when asked to recite at a fast speed. You can help your child learn facts better by letting him or her engage in activities, such as chanting multiplication tables and using fact sheets. The teacher should explain this special treatment to the class, so students will realize that the work is not made easier for your dyslexic child, just accessible.

A smooth integration of children with disabilities into a regular classroom requires good and constant communication. When students can walk in the shoes of disabled children and understand that they are not favored but rather included, the integration has a big chance of being successful.

Chapter IV: Doing Your Part in Your Child's Treatment

A dyslexic child struggles with phonics. Of course, phonics is not the whole picture. Your child has to recognize the sight words, and will need plenty of multisensory and reading activities. His or her dyslexia is also making things, such as following instructions and sequences, difficult. Your child will need extra help in those areas, too.

Dealing with rhyming words

Visualizing and rhyming can be virtual lifelines when you are dealing with dyslexia. You must prepare the handiest memory joggers available to help your child master words. The recommended activities below are great for anybody.

>Single letters

Remembering all 26 alphabets can be problematic. You need to give your child plenty of practice with the sound and look of every letter before he or she can memorize all of them. You can run through the "A is for apple" activity and flip through the alphabet books. However, an even better approach is to bring the letters alive. Draw pictures into them, and turn some of them into quirky characters.

An easier way to help a dyslexic child learn the 26 letter sounds is by teaching 26 images. Help your child recall the letters by transforming them into visual images that he or she can feel. Vowels are tricky, especially for dyslexic children, because every vowel has at least two sounds, short and long. They can also make other sounds when grouped together with the other letters. Focus wholly on vowel-specific visual images and sounds.

A dyslexic child normally has difficulty facing letters the right way, with b and d causing the most trouble. Here is a way to remember b and d in one cute image:

>>Ask your child to touch the tips of his or her thumb, and forefinger together on each hand – making a circle.
>>Point the remaining fingers straight up together, creating a "b" shape with the left hand and a "d" shape with the right.
>>Explain to your child that the bed image can help him or her remember which way "b" and "d" face.
>>Draw a blanket and pillow on top of yours, and ask your child to do the same with his or her picture.
>>Write the word bed in the picture with the sides of the bed serving as the vertical lines in "b" and "d," and then sound it out so your child hears the letter sounds. Make her do the same.
>>Tell your child to do this image every time he or she forgets "b" and "d."

>Spelling

When letters join together, they can keep their sounds, but still, blend smoothly. They can also create new sounds that you have to get to know anew, such as ir and ch. Some of the most common letter clusters are bound by easy-to-grasp rules. Dyslexic children need to learn a few rules, so they can impose order on the letters that otherwise make no sense to them.

Notice the pattern in pin and pine, mad and made, and hop and hope. When you add "e" to the end of words, the "e" bosses the earlier vowel into saying its name out loud. This rule helps your child read and write tons of words. "E" is a special letter. When it is on the end of a word, it shouts out its name.

Here is another old-school spelling rule that just about everyone has heard of: "i ('eye') before e ('ee') except after c ('see') unless you hear 'ay' (like in neighbor and weigh)." This verse can come in handy because it can help your child understand pretty challenging spellings, such as perceive, receive, and receipt, and eight and neighbor, too.

>Sight words

You see the word "they" almost every time, so it is a word that your dyslexic child must know early on. Edward W. Dolch decided to count the frequency of the most commonly used words back in the '50s, and created a list of 220 of the most common words of all. Since then, teachers have used this list to help kids get "sight" recognition of the most common words.

You have probably heard teachers call them "sight" words. The easiest way for your child to learn to write or read a new word is to read and/or write it plenty of times. Make your child do this by running through these activities using only ten sight words at a time:

>>Write down ten sight words on ten pieces of paper. Ask your child to spread them out facing down, and make

him or her turn every word over, read it, and then write it on a paper.

>>Have him or her place ten words into a stack, and ask him or her to turn over each one, read it, and write it down.

>>Ask your child to choose a word as you hold the words in a fan facing you, read it, and write it down.

>>Hold the ten words in a fan facing you, and then ask your child to choose – without looking at a word – and take three guesses at which word he or she picked. If guessed correctly, your child reads it and writes it down. If incorrect, it goes back into the fan. Keep going until your child is done with all ten words.

These activities only take five or ten minutes. Ask your child to put the ten words they picked into an envelope and do any or all daily activities for a week. Bedtime or breakfast are great times, by the way. At the end of each week, your child will be right at home with those words. If not, come up with words your child still struggles with and put them into the envelope to comprise part of his or her next ten words.

You can use fewer words if you think it will work better for your child. Do not use more than ten words. Dyslexic children recall graphic images far better than written words. It makes perfect sense for them to transform words into images whenever they could. Sight words like "walk," "jump," and "eat" are ideal for this. Your child can put eat on a plate, draw a pair of feet to the bottom of the "k" in "walk," or make letters jump out of "jump."

>Words that sound alike

A lot of words sound alike but are spelled differently. This may confuse your child to no end. Words that sound alike are called homophones or homonyms. You may also hear the term homographs, too. Below is a quick explanation of these three terms:

>>Homonym: It is a general term for words that sound alike but do not have the same spelling, in spelling but not sound, or in both sound and spelling.
A general term for words that are the same in sound but not in spelling (like son and sun), in spelling but not sound (like a bow in your hair and bow of a ship), or in both spelling and sound (like grave in a cemetery and grave as in serious). Homographs and homophones are subsets of the bigger, general term "homonyms."
>>Homophone: It is a subset of homonym. Homophones are words that sound alike but spelled differently.
>>Homograph: It is another subset of homonym, where words are spelled the same but pronounced differently.

How can you help your dyslexic child spell and read the common pairs of words that sound-alike? Take note of the following tips:

>>Help your child place words in "families," which are sets of words with the same ending. For example, tight, bright, light, might, and sight. Your child will remember one written pattern and generates tons of words from it.
>>Make sure your child understands what every word in the pair means. If it is appropriate, help your child determine which word is more common. When they learn the common spelling first, they know which situations it does not apply to.
>>Help your child highlight parts of words that sound out in unusual ways or do not sound out. This will help

him, or her learn these words by their visual appearance. It will help to use colored highlighter pens, but underlining or encircling the letters will work, too. Encourage your child to mark any word in any way that will help him or her remember it better.

Getting used to phonics

Phonics is a teaching technique that lets children discover that the letters represent the sounds they hear inside the words. It is the backbone of learning to read. This is why you must guide your child through it thoroughly and systematically.

>Letter sounds

Ensure your child knows the sound of every letter of the alphabet when leading him or her through phonics. If your child already knows the letter names, tell him or her to forget them for now and talk of "a", "buh", and "cuh" instead. Once he or she can sound out a few consonants, and short sounds of the vowels, then you know your child is ready to put them together into three-letter words.

Help your child learn consonant sounds by drawing features into every letter and turn it into an individual character that behaves distinctively. Multisensory learning offers a great way for dyslexic children to learn. When your child learns vowel sounds, begin by teaching only the short sounds: a as in apple, e as in egg, i as in ink, o as in octopus, and u as in up. He or she will learn the long vowel sounds later and the other vowel combinations (like ei and er). For kids younger than grade 2, you can add this game to your activities:

>>Cut a sheet of paper into 20 pieces, about 1 x 2 inches in size for each.
>>Write a vowel on every card and leave four cards blank.
>>Draw a smiley face on every blank card.
>>Ask your child to hold the cards facing down, overturn them one by one, and tell you every letter sound as each card is turned over.
>>If your child turns over a smiley face card, then he or she will clap three times, run to the door, and knock on it.
>>You can also make the smiley cards mean any kind of action, depending on the available space and your child's age.

>Three-letter words

The first words that your child utters by himself or herself usually are short-vowel, phonetically-regular words that sound out the way they expect them to. How do you help your child move from single-letter sounds to reading the complete words? Get an index card, cut it into half. On one half, write "a", "t" on the other. Give them to your child and do the following:
>>Ask him or her to tell you their sounds
>>Put down the "a" and slide "tuh" next to it, and say each sound as he or she moves it.
>>have your child do this a few times until they hear the word "at" and get the core of reading – that letters represent the combined sounds to create words.

Once your child is well-acquainted with "at," he or she is ready to meet the members of the "at" word family. The next activity below will show you how to make your child build the eight words (bat, cat, fat, hat, mat, rat, pat, and sat) by joining letters onto "at":

>>Ask your child to write "at" on an index card.
>>Get four more index cards and cut each of them in half.
>>Write the single letters b, c, f, h, m, p, r, and s on one of the cut index cards, and give them to your child.
>>Ask him or her to place "at" down in front of him or her.
>>Make him or her slide every single letter in front of "at" and read the words he or she produces.

>Blended consonants

Your child is now ready to read consonant blends, such as st, bl, and str in phonetically-regular words. Blending describes how your child can blend letters together to read whole words. However, the consonant blends are chunks of two or three consonants. Your child needs to read, and hear the blend in the first column, and then whiz through the words in the next column. He or she may want to read the table in three separate sessions, or blast through them in one go.

Blends and their examples:

>>bl: black, blimp, blocks, blot
>>br: Brad, brick, brag, bring
>>cl: clamp, clasp, cliff, clock
>>cr: crab, craft, crisp, crust
>>dr :draft, drop, drink, drum
>>fl: flag, flash, flick, flood
>>fr: Fred, frog, fry, frost
>>gl: glad, gloss, glen
>>gr: grand, grin, grass, grip, grub

>>pl: plan, plant, plug, plod
>>pr: prick, prod, print
>>sk: sketch, skip, skin, skunk
>>sl: slant, slim, slip
>>sm: smack, smell
>>sn: snap, snip
>>sp: spank, spill, spell, spin
>>spl: splash, split
>>spr: spring, sprint
>>st: stack, stand, stand, stem, stop
>>str: string, strip
>>sw: swell, swill, swing, swim
>>tr: trap, trip, trend
>>tw: twig, twist, twin

Your child may need extra practice with ending blends. If this is the case, get a piece of paper or whiteboard, ask them to write the relevant words and underline the combinations. When the tricky letters are highlighted, it will be easier for your child to read the words.

Blends and their examples:

>>Ct: fact, inspect, pact
>>Lk: bulk, milk, silk
>>Mp: bump, hump, jump, lamp, stump
>>Nd: band, fend, land, lend, stand, trend
>>Ng: bang, bring, fling, lung, ring, tang
>>nk: blink, chunk, sink, skunk, think, wink
>>nt: bent, blunt, sent, spent, tent
>>sk: ask, mask, risk, task, tusk
>>st: best, frost, list, mast, nest, past, test, trust

>Digraphs

A digraph is a spelling/sound chunk made by two combined letters to create a distinctive sound. The consonant digraphs are sh, ch, th, and ph. The wh can be considered a digraph, as well.

When your child checks out the books, he or she finds all sorts of easy and difficult words there. You can help your child deal with them by learning the digraphs. You may want to tell him or her that th has two sounds: one for words like then and this, and another for words like thin and thank. Several sight words include digraphs and maybe a bit tricky for your child to sound out. It is worth it for your child to know the sight words because they are used often in the English language.

>Tricky vowel sounds

Vowels represent two sounds: short and long sounds. They can join together with the other letters to create a few more sounds. Short vowel sounds are sounds you hear in egg, apple, ink, up, and octopus. Meanwhile, the long vowel sounds you hear in ice, eve, ape, uniform, and open. The long sounds are also sounds you hear when you mention the letter names.

One special letter you will need to point out to your child is the letter y. This letter makes its simple alphabet sound in words like yam and yellow. However, in words like mystery and merry, it makes the sounds made by long e, and the short and long i. This letter sounds typically like long e on ends of words with more than one syllable.

The letter y is seen in the middle, or almost the middle, of a few words. Tell your child to watch out for it, because it means that an i sound, short or long, is formed. The best way to help your child understand the sound being made is to try out the short i sound first. Whenever y comes after g or c, it makes those letters produce their soft sounds. Some short one-syllable words sound like long i when it is the last letter in the word.

A strategy that can help your dyslexic child recall a group of words – like type, style, and python – is to have a personal dictionary. Your child will write groups of words and add new group members as they come across them. There are no hard and fast rules for spelling these words, but bunching them together helps a lot.

When your child utters words, like around and ago, he or she pronounces the first "a" as "uh." This sound is called a schwa, and you have to tell your child about it, so he or she will not spell the words ugo and uround. You do not need to mention the technical stuff, though. Just say that, sometimes, the letter "a" has an indistinct "uh" sound.

The schwa is the technical term for an unstressed vowel sound. It is easiest to hear in the vowel "a," but the other vowels can be schwa sounds, too. Help your child read the fuzzy sounds by making him or her pronounce them phonetically, and correct himself or herself.

Your child needs a firm grip on the vowel+r spelling, as well, as it often crops up and its sound is not the straightforward blended sound of the two letters. Make sure to have your child learn that er, ur, and ir all sound the same. Once your child discovers the sound that these digraphs make, ask him or her to highlight the digraphs in every word, sound them out, and read the words to you.

Ask your child to write the words you dictate. Have him or her jot down the possibilities, in case he or she gets stuck writing a word, to check whether your child can spot the correct-looking spelling. Reveal the correct spelling if your child cannot determine the right one, and ask him or her to jot it down a few more times.

>Consonants

You must show your child the common sounds that consonants make when they join together with other vowels or consonants. The z sound that the letter s makes on the end of "friends," and the soft sounds made by g and c may confuse your child.

A single letter that you may want your child to learn is s. In words like "hands," "friends," "dogs, and "loves," your child hears the z sound but sees the letter s. In words, like horses and foxes, your child sees es, but hears the iz sound. When your child finds a word that does not follow the rule, tell him or her to see it as an all-by-itself word, or check whether he or she can find a few other words similar to it and create a new word family.

If your child skipped or jumped, he or she did two things that end with "t" sound, but spelled as –ed. Tell your child that this ending can sound like "ed" when used in words like "chatted" or "smiled." Once they learn that g and c make soft sounds "jee" and "see," they may begin switching between soft and hard sounds erratically.

Here are some general reading tips:

>>Break the words into syllables.
>>Highlight tricky parts.

>>Check for spelling rules.

Here are some writing tips:

>>Sound out the word in your head, from beginning to end, as well as in syllables (if your word has more than one syllable).
>>Write down the possible spellings of a sound before you commit to one.
>>Encourage your child to write down the spelling possibilities he or she thinks of, even if you find some of them impossible.
>>Exaggerate the pronunciation if it helps.
>>Listen for short and long vowel sounds so that you can use the spelling rules.

Using kindness to manage your child's difficulties

Helping dyslexic children is about modifying their surroundings, and accommodating their needs, instead of forcing things on them. If your child struggles with a book, find another book and find better ways to make things easier. When your child reads aloud to you and gets stuck on a word, give the correct answer right away, and continue reading.

Difficult words are not worth battling. Your dyslexic child will discover them by reading them often, and you can help by making your child write the words down on paper and read them to you daily for several days. You may post them on your walls, as well. Never interrupt the flow of your child's reading to make him or her figure out all the difficult words.

Your child should first feel secure to make headway with his or her reading skills. When you are reading with your child, here are some tips to know when it is fine to take a time out and make your child figure out words that he or she gets stuck on:

>The interruption does not make your child forget what is going on in the text.
>You know your child can sound out the word, as long as you prompt him or her.
>You have not stopped to figure out words tons of times already.
>Your child is receptive.

Contextual cues serve as clues for your dyslexic child to know the meaning of the text, and the words they may expect to see from the diagrams, subheadings, and keywords. Here are a few suggestions on how you can ensure that you are using all those helpful cues:

>Cover blurb: You may use this to help you determine what books you wish to read.
>Table of contents: Your child must first check the table of contents to get a rough idea of what is coming from the chapter headings.
>Subtitles: If your child sees words, such as "horse" or "boy," then he or she knows that the text is more likely about a boy and a horse than a woman getting robbed.
>Introduction: Have your child read the introduction of a book.

>Key words: Words become essential when they are repeated in the text. Have your child look for nouns that frequently appear.

>Pictures and diagrams: Any images that your child could find in text are helpful. Help your child get into the habit of looking at these every time they appear.

>Grammar: Your child could use the grammatical cues when they are in the middle of reading.

Using contextual cues during reading is a secondary reading skill. If your dyslexic child relies excessively on them and forgets to sound out the words, then his or her reading is all over the place.

Multisensory learning

You need to first play the role as a partner or facilitator before helping your child with multisensory learning. Make sure to replenish suppliers of materials and join the activity but take a facilitating instead of a lead role. Your child has control and ownership of a task and will feel more inclined to get right into it. Here are easy ways to let your child assume ownership of his or her learning and get multisensory:

>Ask your child to hold a pen, paper, and a book. Your child must feel that the work is his or her work and not just something you wish him or her to do.

>Keep a schedule and remind your child to follow it.

>Offer help in small doses, but only when needed.

>Make your child take responsibility for the things they do, such as bringing a journal for you to sign, or sharpening a pencil.

>Give small responsibilities to your child at home to make him or her feel independent and valuable.
>Praise your child for completing his or her tasks.
>Teach your child to ask for help in a polite manner. If your child fails to do so, gently remind him or her that a request must be done courteously.

Helping your child get multisensory at home is essential. While your child may receive a lot of spoonfeeding at school, you need to compensate for this at home. Most of what you do will rub off on your child.

Making homework more enjoyable

The idea that kids should do their homework quietly at a brightly-lit desk may not be appropriate for your dyslexic child. You must experiment with many ways of doing things and not force something on your child if it is not working. Try doing it differently, instead. Here are a few tips:

>Allow your child to stand or alternate between sitting and standing to complete a task. Your child may feel more comfortable in switching positions. Movements may also make your child refocus.
>Give him or her brightly-colored highlighter pens, and mark the keywords.
>Allow your child to chew gum or nibble on a healthy snack while doing a task.
>Provide a bookmark to monitor his or her reading progress.
>Allow your child to sip from a water bottle to get the benefit of making small movements to stay focused.

>Help your child represent information in pictures and diagrams.
>Give your child something, such as a seat of beads, to manipulate in his or her hand. Many dyslexic children have difficulty staying still, so this can be helpful.
>Experiment to see whether your child can focus better in a quiet or noisy environment.
>Give your child short breaks. Most kids have a 20-minute attention span, and the same goes for many adults. Frequent short breaks allow a person to enjoy a learning advantage.

Unleashing the happy hormones

Happy hormones run through your veins when you exercise, allowing you to feel great. While it may take a while to push yourself into a physical exercise, you will begin feeling good once you are moving. Educators and psychologists recommend daily practice for struggling readers. Kids who engage in exercise every day do better in writing and ready than those who do not.

Helping your child manage everyday challenges

You want your dyslexic child to feel confident, happy, and loved. Your child needs to know that he or she is okay, despite the condition, and that other people will accept him or her. Here are some signs that your child is suffering from anxiety:

>I always knew I was different.
>I just do not get it, no matter how hard I tried.

>I felt isolated and jealous. Why can't I do the things that other kids can easily do?
>I couldn't find the words I wanted and knew I looked dumb because of it.
>I would find myself at the cupboard without knowing what I had gone there for.
>The teacher would ask me to do something, but I would mix it up.
>I forget people's names, despite having known them for years.
>I could never gauge what time it was, and I could not understand clocks.
>I was never sure if what I thought I heard someone say really was what that person had said.

And, as if all of this were not bad enough, here are the things that people tell dyslexics:

>You never listen.
>You are lazy.
>You do not want to learn.
>Follow the words!
>Your writing is like a kindergartner's.
>Think!
>You will not be able to go to college.
>You need to try harder.
>You have to listen better
>You have to concentrate more.
>You will be held back a grade.
>You will have to look for an easy job.

Children with dyslexia can easily feel below par or weird. This is why parenting must include protecting, building, and repairing a dyslexic child's self-confidence. Your child cannot move forward unless he or she feels productive and valued. You have to step up your nurturing skills to meet your child's needs.

How to listen to your child

Most people think of themselves as good listeners, but only a few of them genuinely are if you ask their friends and families. You can do several things to become a better listener, and most of them do not come naturally to most people, so it is essential to learn them. As a nice spinoff, you get to become a better friend, parent, and teacher.

You have to learn to accept that your listening skills could need an overhaul. Try out these tips the next time your child or a friend talks to you:

>Listen more than you talk – Your child does not want your opinion unless you were asked for it. He or she wants to be heard, so resist the temptation to butt in.

>Never judge. Resist the temptation to say things, such as "that was silly of you." You are encouraging your child to open up to you. If you judge your child, they will stop talking and make a mental note never to confide in you again.

>Encourage conversation. Allow your child to go into the details by paraphrasing what your child says. Never try to clarify what your child says by asking probing questions. Your child will only get annoyed at you.

>Let your child do the problem-solving. Most of the time, children will come up with their own solutions and

strategies. Do not do your child any favor by ruling over her because most fears come from the feeling of no control.

Big kids are more able to solve their problems than the little ones. However, even your little child can think things through when you give a little probing and prompting. Try to keep your child talking for at least 10 minutes, then lift his or her spirit a bit to clear his or her mind. Follow up with action after your conversation, such as asking whether your child wants a hot chocolate or soak in a tub to feel better. Steer your child into saying what he or she will do next.

If you think that your child is not the talking type, then you may want to spend more time with him or her. Hang out with your child. Provide as much therapy as you can to make your child engage in a heart-to-heart chat.

Empowering your child

Help your child solve his or her problems. Instead of providing answers, help your child come up with his or her own. You should also help your child role-play behaviors, such as smiling, listening, and making positive comments that can form friendships. If your child has difficulty making friends, he or she does not want you to point it out. Practice positive behaviors without telling your child that he or she is doing everything wrong.

Your child also needs to explain himself or herself, and your help is crucial. Engaging in many extra-curricular activities can also help improve a child's self-esteem, such as joining clubs or simply having fun with family. Be a receptive listener, so your child comes to you to share his or her problems. Never interrupt, and just listen.

Help your child get rid of unhelpful habits, such as not speaking up for herself or not sharing, without making your child feel responsible for his or her problems. Praise him or her when she does good things. Encourage play dates, too. Make your home a fun place for your child's friends. You should also help him or her deal with bullying, but "stand up for yourself" is not a piece of good advice. Seek help from the school counselor, or other professionals, if you must.

Responding to your child's mistakes

Everyone makes mistakes. However, when your child hardly has any sense of time and space, and cannot follow directions, then he or she will make more. Parents must handle a dyslexic child's mistake as calmly as possible as a stirred-up child feels angry, agitated, or nervous. Try out these tips:

>When bring up a sticky issue, it is best not to be personal and focus on the task. Tell your child what you want, and not what your child has or has not done, so you do not end up criticizing him or her.

>Make sure that you have your child's full attention before giving important directions. Your child must be looking at you, and you should talk to him or her away from distractions.

>Give directions in short and clear sentences, so your child repeats them easily back to you.

>Say things precisely. It will also help to specify whether your child can get his or her own drinks or snacks or whether your child must stay put until you call for breaks.

>Create ways for your child to help you so that she will feel successful and valued. Be extra careful, though, and make your expectations realistic, or your best intentions can backfire.

Teaching directions

A dyslexic child can have difficulty telling up from down, left from right, and the like. He or she may struggle with hand-eye coordination and be unable to do things like drawing a straight line. Things are different with dyslexic children. Remembering the difference between left and right could take weeks or forever.

One method that parents use to help their children learn directions is by using an analog watch. Your child can look at it to be reminded which ways the numbers are facing and know that it sits on the left arm. If he or she wants to go left, then the best way to know is to remember the watch arm.

Spatial terms

Your child struggles to remember the names of familiar things. When it comes to selecting the correct word from tons of conceptually similar words, such as before or behind and over and under, he or she may struggle even more. The best way to help your child with these concepts is to team up for routine activities at home. First, head to the kitchen, where your dyslexic child could flip over the pancake and pour over the syrup. Head outside with a ball, throw it into a hoop, roll it under the chair, and lob it over a trampoline.

Navigation

Other directional concepts may also get into a muddle in your child's mind. Even dyslexic adults often report that they fear going to unknown places, worrying that they may never find their way back. When your child starts school, you need to help him, or her navigate around it.

Explain the situation to the principal or the guidance officer, and schedule a few visits to help your child familiarize himself or herself with the school layout. Pocket maps help older kids, but you must show them how to visualize themselves on the map and use landmarks. The more your child gets used to taking mental snapshots, and the more your child will be able to use it in places outside school.

Improving hand-eye coordination during play

Your child uses a lot of fine motor skills in school that require good hand-eye coordination. He or she manipulates beads, blocks, and other tiny things, as well as scissors along the curves and lines. Good hand-eye coordination does not easily come to people with dyslexia, so prepare your child by having toys and crafts at home and making sure that they use them.

Copying

Copying is difficult for people with dyslexia as their brains do not seem to hold onto the mental image of what they saw. Your child may continuously have trouble copying things, so you need to lend your helping hands. There are two ways to do it:

>First, stick to a routine of helping your child read to identify the words on the board quickly.
>Second, ask the teacher to consider your child's difficulties and make simple accommodations, such as having your child copy only the keywords.

When your child reaches the second grade, handwriting will become another issue. Your child will be asked to practice writing more frequently. The only problem is that your child may never develop winning penmanship. Talk to the teacher and ask for consideration. Explain that you want to ensure that your child does not start to hate school simply because of a skill that he or she can never truly master.

Telling time

Your child may also have trouble figuring out the days of the week, months of the year, and the time of day. This is because your child cannot match the word to the right concept. He or she may not be able to figure out immediately the day, month, or week, even if you tell the answer. Your child may also find it hard to place personal stories into a time frame. Here are tips to help you out:

>Reading a clock

Give your child hands-on activities to learn things better. Telling time lends itself to hands-on discoveries because you could use all kinds of timers. Digital clocks make life easier, but your child needs to understand analog clocks first.

Create or purchase a clock for your child to play with, and explain how the hands work by themselves. Here is a handy rhyme to help your child remember the hands: "The little hand has all the power, it's the one that tells the hour."

Provide plenty of opportunities to practice, and ask your child to repeat explanations back to you. Your child will find a way to organize his or her thoughts when there is ample chance. Teach your child one concept at a time.

>Checking out the calendar

You need to pin your child's personal information to the weeks and months. Have your child create a calendar. Most computers have a calendar program to help your child plot school breaks and birthdays on the months, print them out and staple them together.

Tell your child to cross off the days as they pass. Your child may enjoy looking out about the solar system and how the days and years are measured by it. The key is to personalize and attach physical action to it.

Remembering a sequence

Dyslexic kids often have difficulty expressing linear thoughts, remembering things, and following a line of conversation. Remembering strings of instructions and numbers is a skill, short-term memory, often used in dyslexia assessments. If you think that your child has this difficulty, you can help by breaking the sequence into small steps and then add more only when you are sure that your child thoroughly understands them.

Task analysis is the name that psychologists use to describe the breaking down of tasks into small steps. To be effective in explaining a task sequence to a dyslexic child, you must do the following:

>Make a comparison or an analogy that relates what you are introducing to your child to something they are already familiar with.
>Point out the big features of a new concept before homing in on the details.
>Ask your child to make guesses on a new concept and tell anything that he or she knows.
>Explain the details you are leading up to, but in small bites.

Ask your child broad questions. Have him or her compare new data to what he or she already knows, and make your child take guesses. Your child will become an active learner with this method and gain more self-confidence. Make corrections only when your child can no longer move forward without any interruption. Always remind yourself to stop talking, and step back as your child learns new things.

Maintaining peace and order at home

Your child's self-concept is affected by dyslexia when his or her problem is reading and writing. This, together with struggles in school, affects the entire household. You may worry about your child's frustration and depression and tread warily not to upset him or her.

However, parents of dyslexic children tend to overprotect their kids or expect too much of them. Siblings may resent the extra time you spend with your dyslexic child, and in turn, they may resent the freedom they have. With a dyslexic child in the household, you can find yourself managing a significant and volatile boiling pot.

>Shared responsibilities

Shared responsibilities help households become more orderly. Your dyslexic child must be included in the duty roster to avoid mistakes and misunderstandings. Make sure to choose his or her responsibilities wisely, and choose only the small tasks, such as loading the dishwasher or setting up the table.

>Discipline

Disciplining your dyslexic child can be challenging. Your child may do things that appear intentional, even when they are not. Make a measured instead of an impulsive response. Here are some guidelines for you:

>>Your child quickly forgets instructions, understands them but gets them in the wrong order, or misunderstands instructions. You need to make sure that your child hears and understands what you say.

>>Your child has a fragile ego as his or her dyslexia prevents her from being academically excellent. Your understanding can help your child pass through the bad times. Stay calm and encourage your child to talk about their anger, refocus, and then get busy on other things.

>>Punishing your child can make him or her feel humiliated. Repeated punishments can desensitize your child and make him or her wonder why there is a need to be good anyway. The best response is to look for ways for your child to atone, such as making your child do an extra chore to pay for something that he or she lost or broke.

>>Response immediately to your child's behavior. Ask right away what is going on. If you save your response later, your dyslexic child may not recall the incident you are questioning.

>>Give your child consequences only when you are calm and to solve the problem and not to blame the child.

>>Your responses to your child's misdemeanors should be consistent and firm but manageable. Calmly and clearly tell your child why the behavior is not helpful. Make your consequences helpful and small, and not reactionary and big.

>Sibling love

Here are a few strategies that psychologists recommend to help your children talk respectfully to one another:

>> Ensure everyone in the household understands what dyslexia is about and that your dyslexic child needs enabling instead of protecting.

>>Explain to your other children why their dyslexic sibling needs extra help with school and that all of them will get the help that they need rather than an equal share of things, such as your time.

>>Listen to your children. You can get rid of a child's resentment and jealousy by hearing him or her out. Let your child say how he or she feels, even if it includes hate. Resist the urge to say things, such as "you should not say things like that."

>>In events where your dyslexic child's difficulties make minimal or no difference, make sure to treat your children the same.

Chapter V: Dyslexia: Beyond the Childhood Years

Your teenager is on his or her way to adulthood. He or she is learning tons of new things fast and can make you feel like you were the only one who did not get the memo. How can you help your dyslexic teen feel great when their condition makes people seem him or her as "dumb"? How do you persuade your teen to become more independent? Read on.

Boosting your child's self-confidence

Low self-confidence can block your child's progress. You may have heard this many times, but there are still plenty of important things to keep in mind when you cannot see the nice person behind your teen and feel like throttling:

>I can figure out the problems on my own, if I have enough time.
>I have my own way of tracking school stuff. Please do not move my things.
>I do not deliberately do things wrong or miss doing them altogether. I just get muddled.
>I get frustrated. I wish I can do things perfectly. When I cannot, I do not want to do them at all.
>I try to listen when you talk, but noises distract me.
>When my work is all over the place, remember that I put twice as much effort and time as everyone else.
>If I mess up, I need you to give me a slight hint. Please do not call me lazy or lose your temper with me.
>When you see me acting strong, it is a fair bet that I still feel dumb deep inside.

>It is hard for me to make friends, so please try not to dismiss out of hand the ones that I have.
>Telling me how others do things does not help me. It makes me feel that you do not like me for who I am and wish I were them.
>I have a sense of humor, and it helps me when we joke about my goof-ups and my mistakes.
>I really want to please you.

So how can you build your teen's self-confidence back up? You can do wonders for your beloved child by:

>Maintaining a respectful tone when telling your child that he or she determines his or her own progress, and development, but you can help out, too.
>Having your child tutored and helping him or her learn strategies, like efficient note-taking.
>Helping him or her stay abreast of technology that may help. You can check dyslexia websites to see what is the latest technology can help your child.
>Helping your child feel more independent by making him or her responsible for certain chores and encouraging them to join clubs.
>Working in time for music, sports, and other nonacademic pleasures.
>Keeping your social life, and outside interests so he or she has a good role model.

Going behind the steering wheel

Taking a driving test could be nerve-wracking for anyone. If your teen has navigation issues, and is not so great with hand-eye coordination, he or she may feel anxious by now. Here are some tips to help your teen:

>Help solve the directional problem by using terms such as "passenger's side" and "driver's side" rather than left and right. You can try having your child write the words on their hands, remember where the watch hand is, or place stickers on the car windows.

>Make sure that your child takes plenty of practice written tests.

>Take your child out for practice driving as often as possible.

>Enroll your child in driver education classes.

>Tell your teen to start driving early. He or she can get a learner's permit at age 15 or 16, and may be able to obtain a regular license as early as 16 (in some states).

Go to www.dmv.org for your state's requirements. You can get practice tests and training materials from any DMV office. Most documents are downloadable, as well.

Facing school-related challenges

You pretty much arrange everything for your child when he or she was in elementary school. You anticipate your child's needs, ask the teachers to make considerations for him, and make sure that his or her Individualized Education Program (IEP) goes well. Your role suddenly changes when your child becomes a teen.

You need to hand over the academic reins because your teen now has to prepare and do things on his or her own. Your teen must know his or her own needs, and speak up if need be. What can you do to make the handing over go well? Give your teen kind and frequent reminders for the following:

>Write down to-do lists
>Pinpoint all practical needs
>Use every available gizmo to help him or her read and write
>Ask friends to help your teen in specific ways, like reading texts out loud
>Practice describing his or her dyslexia to tell people about it without feeling embarrassed easily
>Remember that your teen is not sponging off other people, being dumb, or causing a nuisance.
>If someone does not help him or her, remember that somebody else will

Ownership is the key. Doing most of your child's projects will make him or her feel that a bad grade is not a responsibility. Typing exactly what he or she dictates to you and no more, on the other hand, you are genuinely helping and he or she will feel in charge. The work is your teen's alone.

Dealing with all the reading and writing

Dyslexia hits your teen hardest when he or she is reading and writing. By now, your teen has developed plenty of coping mechanisms. Here are a few strategies to help your teen deal with written and reading projects:

>Have a quiet study area. It must be properly-equipped with items like a huge working surface, reference books, pens, a printer, and a computer.
>Plan out the long-term projects by setting interim deadlines in a notebook or on a calendar.
>Ask for extra time to complete projects.

>Read and re-read, all text. Talk about it with friends to ensure you have read it correctly and grasped the gist.
>Find your preferred way of note-taking.
>Get curriculum books in audio.
>Mark books, and worksheets, with highlighting markets. You may also place sticky notes to emphasize the key points.
>Type your projects whenever you can cut down the handwriting load that you have to do.
>Ask a friend to proofread your project.
>Use a spell-checker
>Use a speech-to-text program or any other technology that will make life easier for you.

The importance of note-taking

Your teen must learn to take down notes efficiently. He or she must find out what kind of note-taking method works and what must and must not be jotted down. Your high school student must become good at note-taking, and these tips can help him or her get it right the first time:

>Keep it short. Use a phrase instead of a sentence or a word rather than a phrase.
>Get the meat of the subject and disregard the trimmings.
>Think about what you are going to write, rather than taking notes just to take notes.
>Keep related notes in one book, and not on pieces of paper.
>Use symbols and abbreviations but make sure to use them consistently.

>Jot down most notes in your own words, except for facts and formulas.
>Indent, and number your points.
>Write down a keyword if you miss something, leave space for details, and fill in the blanks later.
>Leave space in case you want to add more notes later.
>Date your notes
>Number your pages.
>Look over your notes after taking them, and add extra details that you recall as important, and rewrite the unclear notes.
>Regularly review your notes for better recall.

If your teen has severe dyslexia, they may want to use accommodations like tape-recording the lessons, having a note-taker or a buddy, or having a teacher giving a written outline that can be added to as he or she listens.

Studying foreign languages

Most young adults in high school and college need a few years of foreign language study to graduate. However, learning a foreign language is difficult for people with dyslexia. Your dyslexic teen needs extra time and help with foreign language projects. These tips may make learning easier:

>The most straightforward foreign language for dyslexics to study are phonetically regular languages (like German) and non-alphabetic ones (like Chinese). German is phonetically-regular as it is a what-you-see-is-what-you-get type of language.

>Take sign language to fulfill language requirements. It is a good option because your dyslexic teen gets used to his or her motor and visual skills, and there is no writing and reading involved. Nearly all US states offer it as a credited foreign language course, but you must check if your school offers it. You can check the Laurent Clerc National Deaf Education Center at http://clerccenter.gallaudet.edu/InfoToGo/051ASL.html for more details.

>The best way to help your teen read and write is to teach him or her a structured phonics program using multisensory techniques. The same methods work for studying a foreign language.

For a teen who is still having trouble with reading and writing in English, and is years below in reading, studying a foreign language can be challenging. You may try to get an exemption from taking such a course, especially if the school does not offer a sign language class.

Planning for college and career

Your child may set his or her sights lower than he or she is truly capable of. You need to be vigilant if there is no vigilant careers counselor to place him or her on the right track. Even if your teen does not want to go to college, they can keep the doors open by choosing school subjects that do not limit him or her. You can help your child start thinking about work skills and how to appeal to potential employers, as well.

Many teens do not visit their career counselors until the last couple of years at high school. Tell your child to take this step early on, and let the counselor know about their dyslexia. The counselor can help your child start thinking about their future, whether it is choosing a career, looking for a part-time job, deciding on a college or university, exploring vocational education programs, or finding out about military options.

The counselor also has information on career or college fairs held in your area and when recruiters will visit the school. If your teen has an IEP, planning for the future is part of it. Since planning is an important detail, you will want to ensure that it is happening.

Developing work skills

Your teen has significant demands placed on him or her at this point in life. He or she must work hard to make good grades in school while spending extra time developing work skills outside school. Your teen makes subject choices in high school and maybe expected to begin completing community service hours to graduate. You can encourage him or her to join in extracurricular activities or help him or her get a part-time job. Obtaining work skills during teen years is crucial as college interview panels and employers want to hear that your teen has impressive work experience.

The best way for your child to develop work skills is through a part-time job. Dyslexic children typically enjoy having evening and weekend jobs, especially if they work with supportive colleagues. Help your teen make great choices, fill out application forms, and do tons of mock interviews. Even though you feel the need to protect your child without suffocating him or her, do not forget that they gain experience through paid work and big kudos from their friends.

Heading off to college

Your child knows what it is like to work harder than other people. He or she is used to spending long hours on projects and can never cruise through tests despite being diligent and bright. As a result, the teachers may have told your teen to set his or her sights low. How can you help your child go to college?

Colleges and universities would like to see the following details about your child:
>Dyslexia assessments
>Academic results
>Community involvement and extracurricular activities

Help your child start a portfolio early on, so they have all the documentation that they need. A portfolio is a file or folder filled with important documents. Ensure that your child places her paperwork into the portfolio as soon as possible once obtained, and produce copies just in case. Your child's transition to college is different from that of most students because he or she must ask the college to make considerations, such as:

>Extra time on tests
>Questions read out loud to her
>Extra time on essays
>Test questions written in large print

>Permission to provide oral, instead of written, answers to test questions

Your child must first qualify for disability services to get accommodations. He or she can do this by submitting the dyslexia assessment results to the student services office of the school he or she is applying to. Even if your child has been assessed, your documentation must be up-to-date.

Most colleges want documents that have been accomplished within three years of college entrance. This means tests like the Wechsler Intelligence Scale for Children, taken when a child is between 5 and 16 years old, may no longer be accepted. Your teen may need to take a new test. Check with your child's colleges of choice and see whether you must get adult tests done now.

If your child has not yet been assessed for dyslexia in his or her school, then you should get an assessment now. Submit a written request to the school administration office. If you wish your child assessed after enrolling in a college, you may have to pay a private psychologist. Colleges can give you a list of psychologists who do dyslexia assessments, but you will not receive financial assistance for the test.

He or she will probably not receive accommodations in college if they did not receive special education in high school. Colleges typically ask for dyslexia test results, as well as a proven history of having been given special education services throughout your child's school years. Students who do not get special education services in high school may qualify for college accommodations only when they have an independent diagnosis of dyslexia that contains recommended accommodations.

Entrance exam

Your child will need to take an entrance test if he or she is going to college. The two most popular tests are the SAT and ACT. What is the difference?

>The ACT, which is the most common college entrance test, will take three hours to complete. It measures how much a student has learned in school. It has up to five components: English, reading, math, science, and an optional writing test. If your child receives a low score, then he or she has the option to retake it several times and even ask for the highest score to be sent to potential colleges. For more information, go to www.act.org.

>The SAT is more of an aptitude test. It takes three hours and 45 minutes to complete. There are three test components: critical reading, writing, and math. Each component is split into three parts, including a timed 25-minute essay (separately-timed). You may hear the SAT called the "new SAT" as the format was updated in March 2005. You may also hear it called the "SAT Reasoning Test" to separate it from the additional subject-specific SAT tests that your child can take.

Like the ACT, your child can retake the SAT many times and ask for the highest score to be sent to prospective colleges. Check out the http://collegeapps.about.com/od/sat/a/SATformat.htm for more information.

Colleges accept both tests, according to traditions and preference. Individual states tend to choose one or the other, but your child can take both. Your teen can get the following accommodations on both tests:
>Extra time
>Testing by herself
>Extra and/or longer breaks
>Questions read to her
>Large-print text
>Permission to use a calculator, computer, or tape recorder

Enlist the help of a school guidance counselor three months before testing to get the accommodations in school. This is because the processing of the needed documents normally takes several weeks. The processes for requesting accommodations on SAT and ACT are similar.

>For ACT accommodations, the guidance counselor, must help you complete a request form from the national ACT office. You must choose between two forms:
>>The Application for Extended Time National Testing Form – enables your teen to have more time to complete the ACT
>>The Request for ACT Special Testing Form – gives your child one-on-one testing with special accommodations, like having questions read out loud to him or her.

You fill out a portion of the form, and then the school completes the rest. The guidance counselor will send the form to the national ACT office, together with proof that your child has dyslexia, and it goes through a review process. The board will then send you and the school a letter that says whether accommodations have been granted.

The guidance counselor will need to help you complete the Student Eligibility Form to apply for SAT accommodations. You will be given two pages of the form to fill out while the school accomplishes the remaining two pages. The guidance counselor will send the form to the College Board, together with proof that your child has dyslexia, and then a review process will take place. The board will send you and the school a letter stating whether your requested accommodations have been granted.

Looking for schools and majors

Your teen must weigh his or her strengths against the career he or she is interested in to check whether they are a good match. If they are not well-suited, then your child must reassess his or her choice. Some people think that people with dyslexia are best suited to engineering and architecture before they have impressive spatial skills and can visualize things in three dimensions. Another field that they believe match dyslexics is the arts, but this may be because singers and actors are in the public eye and many celebrities claim to have dyslexia.

Talk to your child and tell him or her about the different jobs out there, and their pros and cons. Accompany her to job fairs, college nights, and career days at their school. If you have friends in jobs that your child is interested in, then try to arrange some work experience. Your child can opt to apply to three main kinds of colleges:
>Two-year college

>Community college

>Four-year college

To get accepted into a four-year college, your teen must obtain better test scores than he or she needs for a two-year or a community college. The more desirable the school or major, the higher the scores he or she will need. Students must start researching for college options during their junior years in high school. Your child must ask the school guidance counselor for assistance in finding good colleges, the qualifications needed,and the disability services being offered.

He or she should also visit college websites, as well, and start gathering information. For lists of dyslexia-friendly institutions, visit the Dyslexic Adult Link website (www.dyslexia-adults.com/a16.html), and the LD Resources (www.ldresources.org). For other college-related concerns, check out the Colleges of Distinction website (www.collegesofdistinction.com).

Disability programs

Your teen can know more about how the colleges of their choice can meet their needs as a person with dyslexia by contacting the student or disability services office. Every college campus has one, or something similar, that gives the same disability assistance. Your child must know how vital the college's disability services are.

Here are the types of services usually offered:

>If a college has a comprehensive disability program, it gives your child plenty of help that may include a learning center and available disability staff members.

>If a college offers disability services, it gives your child help, but probably not the comprehensive type. If he or she requires minimal assistance, then this may be fine for your child. He or she must ask the office additional questions, such as:

>>Does the school have a writing lab or other facilities that can help me?

>>Can I make arrangements for accommodations with each of my professors?

>>Will disability services allow me to talk to my professors, if necessary?

>>Do I have to fill out paperwork in order to receive disability services?

Dealing with applications and interviews

All students, dyslexic or not, competently want to fill out application forms, write impressive essays, and breeze through the interviews. For your dyslexic child, those tasks could take additional commitment and preparation. Your child's college application tells everything about him or her in concise but glowing terms.

>Filling out forms

Help your child read and re-read, through the application forms before filling them out. Proofread his or her answers when he or she is done. Fields that your child will most likely see on a form are the following:

>>Application fee
>>High school transcript (the school fills out this section)
>>Admission test scores (your child will write his or her SAT and/or ACT test scores)
>>Letters of recommendation and the essay
>>Interview (your child will be informed that an interview will be needed)

>Writing an essay

Essays supplement the college application forms and give a college more idea of your teen's kind of person. He or she should make an early start on the essay, so he or she leaves time for several edits and for getting the help of a proofreader. Here are more helpful tips:

>>Write the essay in the active voice.
>>It must be something new and not a rehash of things already said elsewhere in the form.
>>Less is more. Make the essay clear and clean. Does it feel interesting and upbeat?

>Passing interviews

A college notifies a student about an upcoming interview when they are considering accepting him or her into one of its programs. When called for an interview, your child must prepare, and here are the questions that the panel normally asks:

>>What can you offer to this college?
>>Do you think you are prepared for college life?
>>Do you have good study skills?
>>Why do you want to choose this major?

>>Why do you think you will be a good teacher/mechanic/caregiver?
>>Can you tell me more about your interests/work experience/ community service?
>>Do you have any questions?

Dyslexic children may have difficulty answering in an interview if they are prone to forgetting their words. You can help your child feel confident about the interview by jotting down the answers to questions he or she might give. Make sure that your child learns to:
>>Talk at a regular speed.
>>Remember key phrases (which he or she can jot down on index cards).
>>Place his or her hands loosely on the lap, instead of flinging them afar or wringing them together.
>>Say "I will" and not "I'll try to"
>>Iron out nervous ticks, such as swinging a crossed-over leg or tapping the foot.
>>Lose words like "like" and "um"

The more practice your child gets, the more comfortable and confident he or she will feel. Be generous about going through the routine with him or her often. You may also want to talk about the interview attire, as well, and courtesies like waiting to be offered a seat upon entering the interview room and shaking hands. It is best to keep the questions general unless there is a disability staff member or somebody interested in disabilities. Your child must direct all disability-related concerns to the people in the disability services office.

Picking the school

Your child may find that one school that he or she feels right out of all the options. He or she will most likely be torn between a few schools, but the choice may boil back down to that "feels right" factor. In the meantime, your child's decision must include consideration of the following:

>Course content: The subjects must interest him or her, and the test requirements should be reasonable.
>Structure of classes: Small tutorial classes may spark your child's interest more than lectures given to big audiences.
>Disability support services: He or she should check whether the services she receives are low key or comprehensive enough for their needs.
>Dorm and social life: Does your child want to live away from home? Does she play sports? Does he or she want to get a job to help pay for the college tuition? Your child will want to answer these questions and may want to spend time hanging out on campus before making a decision.

Seeking financial assistance

Most scholarships and fellowships are reserved for students with unique talents. Financial aid programs and scholarships are also available for dyslexics, so you and your child must find them. Here are great starting points:

>The Vocational Rehabilitation Office in your area can help with about anything to do with work, finances, and college. Visit their website at www.jan.wvu.edu/sbses/vocrehab.htm for more information.

>The HEALTH Center of George Washington University is the clearinghouse of postsecondary education for people with disabilities. Check their website at www.heath.gwu.edu or call 800-544- 3284 or 202-973-0904.

>Octameron Associates is a consulting and publishing firm for higher education. They sell small and inexpensive books filled with scholarship contacts, as well as application tips. Visit their website at www.octameron.com, or call 703-836-5480 for information.

>You and your child may wish to check out the information on two scholarships that are available annually. The Marion Huber Learning through Listening Awards (six awards) offers financial assistance of $2,000 or $6,000, and is administered through the Recording for the Blind and Dyslexic (www.rfbd.org or 800-221-4792). The Anne Ford Scholarship of $10,000, meanwhile, is administered through the National Center for Learning Disabilities (www.ld.org/awards/afscholarinfo.cfm or 212-545-7510).

Your child can apply for government aid because of financial need, and not dyslexia, and does not have to be very low income to qualify. The U.S. Department of Education's Free Application for Federal Student Aid forms must be accomplished and submitted to the agency. His or her Expected Family Contribution is assessed upon submission. If the expected college costs are higher than the EFC, then you will get subsidized loans. Learn more about the loans available by visiting www.fafsa.ed.gov and www.studentaid.ed.gov.

Dyslexia in adulthood

Some people prefer not to disclose their condition in the workplace. Some employers know about it informally because their dyslexia hardly makes any difference. Others explain their situation upfront before even starting the job. There are places you could call for in-depth advice, but here are the basic things you should know:

>The Americans with Disabilities Act will protect you and your child. It bans discrimination in employment against people with disabilities.
>Section 504 of the Rehabilitation Act will protect you, as well. It bans discrimination against people with disabilities in federally-funded activities and programs.
>Your workplace must give reasonable accommodations to let you do your job.
>If you can do essential work functions, you cannot be legally disqualified or discriminated against because of your dyslexia.
>Your dyslexia must stay confidential and not be disclosed to fellow workers without your explicit consent.

Building a family

Dyslexic children get called lazy sometimes. Their teachers think that they can read if they put in more effort. If parents believe the teachers, they may follow suit. The dyslexic child, as a result, feels awful and grows up looking forward to leaving school early and never reading again.

Years later, however, they will have children, and the spouse thinks he or she is okay. Their child wonders why the dyslexic parent never signs his or her cards and assumes they do not care. This is just one of the scenarios that may happen when a parent keeps their dyslexia a secret.

Letting your loved ones know what is going on is always better than hiding it. You risk weakening your bonds with them if you deceive them. Besides, once they know about your condition, you may be able to laugh at your mistakes with them.

People with dyslexia are genuinely inventive and resilient because they know that they have to be. They will not feel disheartened when there is ample support from people around them. Dyslexic people are capable of becoming successful, too, just like anybody else. They can come to terms with their condition and eventually even manage to chuckle about it.

Downloadable Courses

First off, thanks for buying this book. As promised, here's your package 2 bonuses! Enjoy!
http://howtobeon.top/bonuses/bonus2/

Package 1 and 3, can be found here:
http://howtobeon.top/freebies/

The authors, publishers, and distributors of this guide have made every effort to ensure the validity, accuracy, and timely nature of the information presented here However, no guarantee is made, neither direct nor implied, that the information in this guide or the techniques described herein are suitable for or applicable to any given individual person or group of persons, nor that any specific result will be achieved The authors, publishers, and distributors of this guide will be held harmless and without fault in all situations and causes arising from the use of this information by any person, with or without professional medical supervision The information contained in this book is for informational and entertainment purposes only It not intended as a professional advice or a recommendation to act

No part of this book may be reproduced or transmitted in any form whatsoever, electronic, or mechanical, including photocopying, recording, or by any informational storage or retrieval system without express permission from the author

Made in the USA
Las Vegas, NV
05 February 2022

43245520R00080